It's another Quality Book from CGP

This book is for anyone studying AQA GCSE Product Design.

It explains all the technical details you'll need to understand, with plenty of full-colour diagrams to help make everything crystal-clear.

We've also included advice to help make your project a winner, plus tips on how to improve your exam technique.

What CGP is all about

Our sole aim here at CGP is to produce the highest quality books — carefully written, immaculately presented and dangerously close to being funny.

Then we work our socks off to get them out to you — at the cheapest possible prices.

Contents

SECTION FIVE — SOCIAL AND ENVIRONMENTAL ISSUES

SECTION SIX — PROCESSES AND MANUFACTURE

Published by CGP

Editors:
Katie Braid, Polly Cotterill, Katherine Craig, Ben Fletcher, Helena Hayes, Sarah Hilton,
Adam Moorhouse, Ali Palin, Hayley Thompson, Caley Simpson.

Contributors:
Anne Ainsworth, Ryan Ball, Tim Fulford.

With thanks to Phillip Holton for the content review.
With thanks to Paul Anderson and Katherine Reed for the proofreading.

With thanks to Laura Stoney for the copyright research.

ISBN: 978 1 84762 354 6

www.cgpbooks.co.uk
Clipart from Corel®

Photograph on page 3: 'Red/Blue Chair' by Gerrit Rietveld © SCALA, Florence. The Museum of
Modern Art, New York, 2014.

Photograph on page 3: 'Carlton' by Ettore Sottsass, 1981 — Memphis Milano/Aldo Ballo.

KITEMARK and the BSI Kitemark device are reproduced with kind permission of The British Standards
Institution. They are registered trademarks in the United Kingdom and in certain other countries.

Page 26 contains public sector information published by the Health and Safety Executive and licenced
under the Open Government Licence v3.0.

Photographs of original oak furniture by Neil Connor on page 35 reproduced by kind permission of Anja
Connor.

With thanks to Science Photo Library for permission to use the images on page 3 (Chrysler Building)
and page 67 (wind-up radio).

FAIRTRADE Mark on page 69 © Fairtrade Foundation.

Every effort has been made to locate copyright holders and obtain permission to reproduce sources.
For those sources where it has been difficult to trace the originator of the work, we would be grateful for
information. If any copyright holder would like us to make an amendment to the acknowledgements,
please notify us and we will gladly update the book at the next reprint. Thank you.

Printed by Elanders Ltd, Newcastle upon Tyne.

Based on the classic CGP style created by Richard Parsons.

Project Advice

Unlike most subjects, in D&T you actually get to make something useful (well, hopefully).

The Project is Worth 60% of your GCSE

1) Your D&T project is called 'the controlled assessment'.

2) Your teacher will give you as much help as they're allowed to by the exam board, so do ask them... but mostly it's up to you to make a good job of your project.

3) You can dip into this book for a bit of extra help. Section 1 is all about the design process, so if you're not sure where to start, that might be a good place to look.

4) If you're wondering about a particular detail — what type of board to use, say — it's probably quickest to look that up in the index and go straight to those pages.

Only Put Relevant Stuff in your Folder

Your teacher will give you plenty of guidance on what needs to go in your folder, but here are some tips:

1) The folder should be no more than 20 sheets of A3. You'll lose marks if you do much more than that.

2) So DON'T waste space on irrelevant stuff, especially at the research stage. For example:

> Say you've analysed some existing chairs to see what materials they use...
>
> Don't bore the examiners stupid with detailed descriptions of every chair within a ten mile radius of your school.
>
> A brief summary of your research findings is all that's needed — then the really important thing to say is how those findings helped you decide which materials to use in your product.

3) DO put in lots of photos. The examiners love this. They want to see photos of:

- Any models you make (see p. 10-11). Don't just put in photos of the ones that worked. In fact, the ones that didn't quite work are more useful because then you can explain what was wrong and how you fixed it.

- The intermediate stages of making your final product — part of the way through the assembly process, say — to show how you constructed it.

4) CHECK that you've used the right technical words and spelled things correctly. And make sure you've explained things clearly — get someone who knows nothing about your project to read it and see if it makes sense.

Here's me with the manufacturer's specification.

The Exam is Worth 40%

1) In the exam you'll be tested on everything you've learned during the course — materials, tools, how to design things, how to make things, health and safety, environmental issues...

2) This book can help you learn all that stuff — and has questions for you to check what you know.

3) There's a glossary at the back of the book, in case you need to sort out your thermosetting plastics from your thermoplastics.

4) The exam technique section (pages 86-89) has some worked examples of exam-style questions, and some hints on how to make sure you get top marks.

Controlled Assessment — nope, it's not funny...

When your project is marked, only about a third of the marks are for the final thing you've made and how good it is. Most of the controlled assessment marks depend on the sheer brilliance of your folder.

Evolution of Product Design

Products are always changing — this is known as product evolution, and there are lots of reasons for it.

Manufacturers Try to Continually Improve Products

1) Manufacturers are always looking for ways to make more money. One way to do this is by improving how they make their products, e.g. improving the design so that the product can be made more easily. This is called 'Continuous Improvement'. It's a big reason why products evolve.

2) Manufacturers want their products to be as good as possible — to make money, to be competitive and to meet standards of product quality such as ISO 9000 (see page 65).

3) Manufacturers also redesign products in response to market pull or advances in technology...

Market Pull is About What Consumers Want

1) Designers often design stuff (and manufacturers make it) to satisfy the wants and needs of consumers — consumer demand.

2) Changing fashions and social attitudes affect the kind of products people want — consumer demand won't always be for the same things or styles.

For example, the car was invented to transport people from A to B, but now some consumers expect it to be more of a status symbol, demanding luxury extras like air conditioning, stereos and seat-back TV screens.

Technology Push is About What Manufacturers Can Provide

In industry, research and development departments are always coming up with new technologies, materials and manufacturing techniques. This can drive the design of new products.

1) Manufacturers can use new technology to develop new products, or to improve existing ones.

2) Using new technology might make an existing product cheaper, better at its function or nicer-looking — all things which will make products more desirable.

For example, computers started off as huge mechanical 'adding machines'.
Now, thanks to technologies including the microchip, they're small but really fast and powerful.

Products Can Evolve for Other Reasons

Sometime products evolve because there's a social or cultural need...

Trevor Baylis heard that educational radio broadcasts might help stop the spread of AIDS in Africa. But many rural areas didn't have electricity so couldn't use radios. So Baylis designed and made a wind-up radio that didn't need an electricity supply.

...or because there's a political or environmental need:

Environmentally friendly products are becoming popular — many consumers are put off buying products that waste resources or can't be recycled. Designers have to take this into account with new products. For example, car manufacturers now aim to produce cars with improved fuel-efficiency, e.g. with hybrid engines that combine a petrol engine and an electric motor. And new cars are legally required to contain a certain percentage of parts that can be recycled.

Nothing's ever good enough...

So, designers often come up with new products because of public demand, or because there's new technology. But designers can also be inspired by previous design movements — see the next page.

Evolution of Product Design

Products also evolve because <u>ideas develop</u>. If lots of people have a <u>similar approach</u> to design, this is called a <u>design movement</u>.

Design Movements Influence Product Development

The `Arts and Crafts` movement was founded by <u>William Morris</u>. The designs for wallpaper, furniture and textiles are often based on patterns found in <u>nature</u>. Furniture in this style is <u>upright</u> and <u>angular</u>. Arts and crafts products are normally made by hand, by skilled craftsmen.

`Art Nouveau` designs are <u>flowing</u> and <u>curvy</u>. They often use <u>floral</u> or <u>insect motifs</u>. Well-known Art Nouveau designers are Louis C. Tiffany and René Lalique.

`Art Deco` was inspired by African and Egyptian art. It involves <u>bold colours</u>, <u>geometric</u>, <u>zigzag</u> and <u>stepped</u> shapes, bold <u>sweeping curves</u> and <u>sunburst motifs</u>. Examples of Art Deco architecture include the <u>Chrysler Building</u> in New York.

`Bauhaus` was a design movement in Germany founded by <u>Walter Gropius</u>. His motto was '<u>form follows function</u>' — he thought that products should be designed with their function as the starting point, rather than their appearance. Furniture in the Bauhaus style often has <u>chrome tubing</u> and <u>black leather</u>.

`De Stijl` was a Dutch Modernist movement. The designs were basic — they used <u>simple shapes</u>, vertical and horizontal lines and <u>primary colours</u>. <u>Gerrit Rietveld</u>'s Red and Blue chair is a well-known De Stijl design.

Gerrit Rietveld c.1923

PHOTO: ALDO BALLO

`Postmodernist` designers rejected the 'form follows function' idea — they thought that <u>style</u> should be the starting point. The <u>Memphis movement</u> was at the height of postmodernism — a famous design is Ettore Sottsass's Carlton cabinet. Memphis designs used many bright, contrasting colours and different materials. Other postmodernist styles include <u>kitsch</u> (tacky and 'tasteless') and extreme <u>minimalism</u> (designs without decorative features).

Practice Questions

1) What is meant by <u>market pull</u>?

2) Arthur is designing an MP3 player. How might <u>technology push</u> affect his design?

3) Give an example of a product that has <u>evolved</u> because of:
   a) a social need,
   b) an environmental need.

4) Outline the main <u>features</u> of furniture made in the following styles:
   a) Arts and Crafts
   b) Art Deco
   c) De Stijl

5) What did the Bauhaus designers mean by '<u>form follows function</u>'?

4

Human Factors in Design

Different people have different <u>needs</u> and <u>values</u> — these are known as <u>human factors</u>.
Designers have to take them into account when designing products for a particular group of people.

Products Need to be Accessible for <u>Disabled Users</u>

Lots of products are specifically designed to help people with <u>disabilities</u>.

1) Some packaging (e.g. for medication) has <u>Braille</u> labelling
to give blind people information.

2) Control buttons can be made brightly coloured and extra large,
so they're easy to find and press. For example, telephones,
TV remotes and calculators can be made with big buttons.

3) Products such as smoke alarms can be designed with <u>visible</u> signals
as well as audible ones so that deaf people can be alerted to fires.

Some people will find it easier to use a calculator with bigger buttons.

4) <u>Instructions</u> can be given in <u>picture</u> or <u>diagram</u> form so that
people who have difficulty reading text can still use the product.

5) Designers also have to think about <u>wheelchair users</u>. For example,
trains and buses need to be designed to have wheelchair access.

People Have Different <u>Cultural</u> and <u>Religious</u> Values

Designers need to cater for people with different customs and beliefs.

1) Some groups of people have different <u>dietary needs</u>. For example,
Muslims don't eat pork and Jewish people only eat Kosher foods.

2) Different groups have <u>customs</u> and <u>celebrations</u> which have
particular products associated with them. For example, American
Thanksgiving is associated with a traditional communal dinner, and
the Hindu festival of Diwali is associated with <u>lights</u>.

3) Different cultures have different ways of doing things. For example,
Japanese people traditionally eat at a <u>low table</u> sitting on the floor.

4) <u>Clothing styles</u> vary — in some cultures it's <u>frowned upon</u> for women to wear revealing clothing.

5) <u>Colours</u> can have meanings, e.g. Chinese brides traditionally wear red because it's thought lucky.

Designers Need to Think About <u>Age Groups</u>

People in different <u>age groups</u> have different <u>physical limitations</u>. For example:

1) Small children and elderly people may not be able to manipulate <u>small parts</u>
and may have difficulty undoing <u>fastenings</u> and opening <u>packaging</u>.

2) Elderly and infirm people might have difficulty <u>holding</u> and <u>using</u> products.
Designers can think about putting large, easy-to-grip handles on, say, cutlery.

Sam was having trouble holding the fish — the handle was too small.

What a needy lot we are...

We're all really different — there's no one product that fits us all. Designers have to bear this in mind.
They need to think about who the product is <u>aimed at</u> and make sure that it's <u>made to suit them</u>.

Human Factors in Design

Ergonomics Means Making the Product Fit the User

Ergonomics is about how <u>easy</u> and <u>comfortable</u> a product is to use.

1) Products need to be designed so that their <u>size</u> and <u>proportions</u> fit the user's needs.

2) For example, a <u>chair seat</u> needs to be the <u>right height</u> off the ground so that the person sitting in it has their feet on the floor and their knees at a right angle. The back of the chair should <u>support</u> the person's <u>back</u> in the <u>right place</u>.

3) Designers use <u>body measurement data</u> (<u>anthropometrics</u>) to make sure the product is the <u>right size</u> and <u>shape</u>.

4) <u>Badly designed</u> products can have <u>long-term health impacts</u>. They might well be safe to use on a day-to-day basis (e.g. there's no risk of losing a limb), but end up causing things like <u>eye strain</u> or <u>backache</u> after long-term use.

Something had gone badly wrong with the proportions of Graham's new table.

Manufacturers Design for 90% of the Target Market

Manufacturers try to design products so that they'll be suitable for <u>most people</u> in the <u>target market</u>. They use <u>anthropometric data</u> to do this. For example, someone designing an office <u>desk</u> might look at a graph showing the <u>heights</u> of a sample of adults aged between 20 and 65.

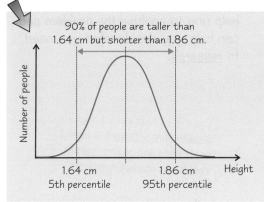

90% of people are taller than 1.64 cm but shorter than 1.86 cm.

Number of people

1.64 cm — 5th percentile

1.86 cm — 95th percentile

Height

1) Manufacturers often try to make 'one size fits all' products. Actually, it's 'one size fits 90%' — they use the <u>5th and 95th percentiles</u> as the cut-off points.

2) This means the <u>bottom 5%</u> (very short people in this example) and the <u>top 5%</u> (very tall people here) <u>aren't catered for</u>. A one-size product wouldn't suit either extreme.

3) These people would probably have to use a specialist supplier or have products <u>custom-made</u> for them.

Practice Questions

1) How can smoke alarms be designed so that they're suitable for <u>deaf people</u>?

2) Explain why some calculators are made with very <u>large buttons</u>.

3) Give one example of a group of people who might have particular <u>dietary needs</u>.

4) Frank is designing a tin opener.
   a) Suggest how he could make sure it's suitable for <u>infirm elderly people</u>.
   b) Explain your answer.

5) a) What is meant by <u>ergonomics</u>?
   b) Suggest what needs to be considered when designing a <u>computer keyboard</u> to make it 'ergonomically' designed.
   c) What might happen to the person using the keyboard if it's <u>badly designed</u>?

6) a) What is <u>anthropometric data</u>?
   b) Suggest what anthropometric data might be needed when designing a <u>football shirt</u>.
   c) Why might a claim that a football shirt is '<u>one size fits all</u>' not be true?

Research and Specifications

The process of designing and making something is called the <u>design process</u> (gosh).

Designing Starts with the Design Brief

So, someone gets an idea for a <u>new product</u>.
They decide to <u>employ a designer</u> to work on the idea.

1) The person who hires the designer is called the <u>client</u>.

2) The <u>client</u> gives the designer a <u>design brief</u>...

3) The design brief is a <u>starting point</u> for the development of the product. It should include:

- what <u>kind</u> of product is needed (and <u>why</u>)
- how the product will be <u>used</u>
- <u>who</u> the product is <u>for</u> (the <u>target market</u>)

DESIGN BRIEF FOR BACKSCRATCHER/TURNIP HOLDER

No currently commercially available backscratcher has an in-built capacity for turnip storage. We want you to design a product to meet this need for those people having itchy backs and modest turnip storage requirements (up to 4 turnips).

In industry, the client supplies the design brief. In the exam, it's the <u>examiner</u>...

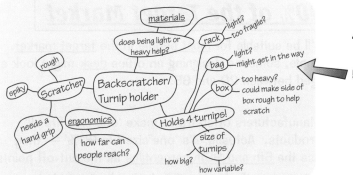

4) You need to pick out all the <u>important features</u> of the design brief.

5) One way of doing this is by drawing a <u>spider diagram</u>. It's a quick way to help you to analyse the problem and can help you decide what you need to <u>research</u>.

Research Helps You Get Ideas

The point of doing research is to:

1) check that people will actually <u>want your product</u>.

2) find out what people in your target market <u>like or dislike</u> about similar <u>existing products</u>.

3) find out what <u>materials</u>, pre-manufactured <u>components</u> and <u>techniques</u> would be suitable for your product, and how they will affect the manufacturing and selling <u>costs</u>.

<u>Spreadsheet software</u> is useful for <u>showing</u> and <u>organising</u> the results of market research.

There are different types of research:

① **Market research** — using questionnaires or interviews to find out people's likes/dislikes and so on. This will help you understand what your <u>target group</u> wants from a product.

② **Product analysis** — you can <u>examine</u> a current product or <u>disassemble it</u> (take it <u>apart</u>) to find out:

- how it's <u>made</u> (e.g. materials, components and processes) and how it <u>works</u>.
- its <u>good</u> and <u>bad</u> features, including how ergonomic the design is (see page 5).
- the <u>size</u> and <u>weight</u> of the product.
- how it tastes, feels, looks or smells (<u>sensory analysis</u>).

Then you should have a good idea of what <u>materials</u> and <u>techniques</u> you need to research for <u>your</u> product.

I've designed your briefs — on to the socks...

Don't just go straight from the design brief to sketching ideas. You first need to check out other <u>similar products</u> already on sale and get some information about your <u>target market</u>. First things first.

Research and Specifications

Use Your Research to Draw Conclusions

Once you've done some product analysis and market research, you should have loads of information. Now you have to use the information to help with your design.

> 1) Summarise what you've found out — pick out the most important and useful findings.
>   E.g. carrots are just as popular as turnips.
>
> 2) Explain what impact each finding will have on your design.
>   E.g. my design should be able to hold carrots as well as turnips.

The Design Specification is a List of Conditions to Meet

1) The design specification gives certain conditions that the product must meet. These conditions (often called design criteria) should take account of your research findings.

2) It's best to write a specification as bullet points. Each point should be explained and show how your research helped you make your decisions. Make sure you've covered the following things:

- Aesthetics — how it looks
- Consumer — who will buy it
- Size — how big it is
- Function — what it will do
- Quality — the required finish
- Cost — the price range
- Environment — the impact on the world
- Safety — how to make sure it's safe
- Materials — what it is made of
- Sustainability — its future impact

Tally chart showing the minimum length of backscratcher that people needed to scratch the middle of their back.

Length (mm)	No. of people
150	I
200	IIII
250	IIII II
300	IIII IIII
350	IIII I
400	IIII
450	

EXAM TIP
In Q1 of the exam you'll have to write and explain design criteria.

Example:
SIZE
- It should weigh 300 g or less, as most people were comfortable with this.
- The minimum length will be 400 mm, as that was long enough for everyone to reach their back.
AESTHETICS
- It should be multicoloured because most people said they would like the product to be very colourful.
- The handle should be easy to grip but not feel rough, because some people were concerned that a rough surface might catch on their clothes.

Practice Questions

1) a) What information does a design brief include?
   b) In industry, who writes the design brief?

2) Read these questionnaire results about the text on a product and write two brief conclusions based on them:
   > Q1. Which colour do you think the text looks best in?
   > Answers: red: 9 black: 18 blue: 24 green: 6
   > Q2. Do you think the size of the text is too small?
   > Answers: yes: 42 no: 15

3) a) What's the point of doing market research?
   b) Describe what you can find out by doing product analysis.

4) a) What is a design specification?
   b) Write a design specification for a combined egg cup/toast rack.

Design Methods and Influences

When you're designing, inspiration can come from almost anywhere...

There are Many Approaches to Designing

Designing is a really complex process and there are several different ways of doing it:

① **Systems Approach** This means breaking down the design process into a number of different stages and doing each in turn. This is a very orderly and reliable method of designing and the one that you will probably use in school.

You don't have to stick to just one of these design methods. Good designers often use bits of all three.

② **Empirical Problem Solving** This means using trial and error to develop a good design. For example, making and evaluating prototypes of different designs until you find one which works pretty well — then making and evaluating prototypes based around that design until you find one that works even better, and so on.

③ **Intuitive Designing** Designers with a lot of experience can make good guesses about what will work well in a design, and what won't. They use this intuition to help them come up with good designs.

You Can Get Inspiration from Patterns...

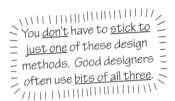

1) Patterns using grids and repeating shapes are often used in product design. For example, fabrics often have a repeating pattern.

2) Many products, especially packaging, are based on simple geometric shapes such as squares, rectangles, circles and triangles.

You can also get inspiration from culture and religion (page 4), by doing a detailed product analysis (page 6) or from other designers and craftsmen. See page 3 for more on the different design movements you could study.

...or Nature

Nature can be a design inspiration for the structure, function or aesthetics (look) of a product.

Structure The domes at the Eden Project are a very strong, lightweight structure, just like a honeycomb.

A honeycomb

The Eden Project

Function Cats' eyes for roads were invented in the 1930s by Percy Shaw. He was inspired by the way cats' eyes reflect light in the dark.

Aesthetics A good technique is the close-up effect. This is where you look at just a small section of an image. For example, you could design some jewellery based on a close-up of part of a flower.

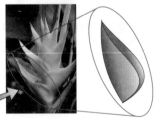

Inspiration for a joke was a bit lacking, sorry...

It makes sense — not everyone works in the same way, so there are bound to be loads of approaches to designing. There are plenty of ways to get inspiration too — even colours and moods (next page).

Design Methods and Influences

Use a Mood Board to Trigger Ideas

A mood board is a collage of images, materials, shapes and colours (rather than actual products) that represents the emotion of a product. They can help to trigger design ideas by giving a visual representation of what people in your target market do and what they like.

1) The images often come from magazines or photos, but you can also use real materials to show texture and finishes (e.g. flat pieces of wood, foil and textiles, or even things like leaves).

2) It's a good idea to add notes to a mood board — for example, you can explain why a certain image is relevant and how it might influence your design.

Designers Also Need to Think About Colour

Colours often represent moods and feelings. This can influence the colours that a designer chooses.

 To create a heavy mood, you might use a dark solid colour...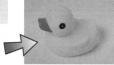

...while for a lighter mood you'd go for a paler colour.

 Colours such as red and orange remind us of fire and the sun and so are known as warm colours...

 ...whereas blues are normally associated with cold.

 Colours you find in nature such as browns, greys and greens are known as neutral colours. They're also associated with calm or relaxation.

Finishes can also influence the feeling of a design — e.g. shiny or metallic finishes can give a high-quality or futuristic feel, but might also seem more impersonal or industrial.

Come Up With Several Ideas and Pick the Best

However you get your inspiration, you need to sketch out a few ideas that meet the design criteria (p. 7). They could all be quite different — let your imagination run wild for a bit... Eventually you'll probably hit on a really good idea. Hurrah. This is the one you should develop further — see the next page...

Practice Questions

1) Outline the main features of these design methods:
   a) systems approach   b) empirical problem solving   c) intuitive designing

2) Ash is trying to design a basin for his friend's new bathroom. Here is the design specification:

- a modern look
- no sharp edges
- less than 50 cm long by 30 cm wide
- must include holes for taps
- easy to clean
- at least 20 cm deep

   a) Suggest something in nature that Ash could use as an inspiration.
   b) How might he use colours to create warmth in the room?

Practical Design and Modelling

Developing your design idea is a really important part of the design process.
Just like revision is a really important stage of the exam process. Hint hint.

Designing is a Circular Process

The design process doesn't stop once you've come up with your first good design.
You should be constantly evaluating (see below) your design and coming up with improvements.

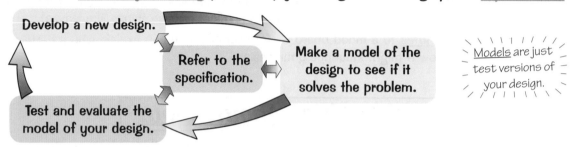

Develop a new design.

Refer to the specification.

Make a model of the design to see if it solves the problem.

Test and evaluate the model of your design.

Models are just test versions of your design.

Detailed Sketches Help You Work Out the Finer Points

1) Your initial sketches will probably have been rough, freehand pencil drawings.
2) Trying out some more detailed drawings is the next stage.
3) It helps you to see what will actually work in practice and it might help you decide on details you hadn't thought about before, e.g. the sizes or positions of components or how parts should be constructed and fitted together.

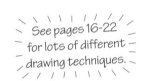

See pages 16-22 for lots of different drawing techniques.

Use Modelling to Improve Your Design

1) Modelling is a good way to spot (and solve) problems with your design.
2) You can make models using materials that are easy and quick to work with, e.g. cardboard, balsa wood or high-density polystyrene foam.
3) Try out different aspects of your design. For example, you could model just one part of the product separately, to check it works, before going on to the rest.

Not that kind...

You can also use CAD/CAM (see page 19) to help with the modelling process.
• You can make virtual models (in 3D) using CAD and easily manipulate things like shape, colour and texture.
• You can use CAD/CAM to do rapid prototyping — draw the design in CAD and use a 3D printer to produce the model.

Test and Evaluate Each Model

After you've made each model, do some tests to check that it's how it should be.
Get some potential customers to try it out and give you feedback too.

1) You'll probably find there are some things that don't work out quite how you'd hoped.
2) Write down what the problem is, suggest how to fix it and try out another version of the model.
3) Record how the design develops — take photos of your models.
4) You should also evaluate each model against the design specification. Take each point on the specification and see if your model is up to scratch.

Test your product on the catwalk...

Testing out design ideas is really important. They might look great on paper, but when it comes to making them they might be totally impractical. Testing them out first avoids expensive mistakes.

Section 1 — The Design Process

Practical Design and Modelling

Modelling Can Help You With Accuracy

Modelling your design can help you work out how accurately it needs to be made.

1) For example, it might not matter if the hands on a clock are a tiny bit too long or too short — it'll still work, and probably look fine.

2) However, accuracy would matter if your product had, say, a door — if you made the door a tiny bit too big it mightn't shut.

3) You can experiment to find out how much margin for error there is — the tolerance (see page 14).

Prototypes Help Manufacturers Avoid Big Mistakes

Prototypes are full-size working products made using the right materials and methods. They're made before industrial production to make sure the product is exactly right — so that money isn't wasted:

1) You can test whether the prototype works properly, is safe, and meets the design specification.

2) You can ask potential end-users (customers) for feedback on the prototype to see whether it meets their needs.

3) If the prototype works well and potential customers like it, a manufacturer would consider going into production on a larger scale.

The final product you make for your controlled assessment is a prototype of your design.

Designs for Mass Production Should be Easy to Make

Designers have to consider how much time and money will be needed to manufacture a product — if products are going to be mass-produced, it's important that they can be made quickly and affordably.

Designs for mass production should ideally:

- Use materials and components which are easily available.
- Use affordable materials and processes.
- Use standard size components.
- Use standard tools, machinery and equipment.
- Use processes that don't require skilled workers.

For one-off products, high quality and individuality are more important and customers are willing to pay more. Therefore, designs can use specialist techniques and equipment, requiring expensive materials and skilled workers.

Practice Questions

1) Alan is developing his design for a toy water pistol. Explain how it could help Alan to draw some detailed sketches of his design.

2) Gabby has designed a jewellery box with different compartments and is making a model.
   a) What is meant by modelling?
   b) Suggest some materials she might use to make her model.

3) Explain how CAD/CAM can help with modelling.

4) a) What is meant by a prototype?
   b) Why might a car company make a prototype of a new car?

5) Sue is designing a digital radio. Suggest some ways she can make the design suitable for mass production, and explain how each of your suggestions would help.

Presenting and Protecting Design Ideas

When you're designing your product you may be thinking about that little island in the Bahamas you're going to buy with the profits. But there are some other things you need to consider too...

Trademarks and Patents Stop People Stealing Ideas

Trademarks

1) Trademarks are distinctive logos, words or slogans that identify a particular company or product. If someone else then uses your trademark you can sue them.

2) Trademarks are shown by the ™ symbol. Individuals or companies can register trademarks with the Intellectual Property Office — they're then shown by the ® symbol.

3) Well known trademarks are Big Mac™ and Microsoft®.

Patents

1) Patents are granted when something new has been invented.

2) They allow the inventor to stop others from making, using or selling the invention without permission. Patents last for 20 years.

3) For a patent to be granted, the invention must involve an 'inventive step' (you won't get a patent for something that's dead obvious), and must be capable of 'industrial application' (something that could actually be made or used in industry).

A good example is cat's eyes which were patented by Percy Shaw in 1934. They contain four glass and metal beads which reflect light back from a car's headlights, showing the driver where the middle of the road is. They're also self-cleaning — as cars drive over them the glass beads are pushed into the casing and rinsed in the rainwater that collects in the base. They're now used in many countries.

Design Ideas Can Also be Protected

Designers can protect their ideas with copyright or registered design.

Copyright (the © symbol)

Any design ideas you produce are automatically protected by copyright. Unless you were working for someone else, you are the copyright owner. If anyone wants to reproduce your work, they have to get your permission. Copyright runs out 70 years after the designer's death.

Registered Design

Registered design protects a new design's shape and appearance, e.g. a car body shape or the design of a mobile phone's casing. This stops other people from copying the design. It only applies to the look of the product, not the way it works. You can register all of the design or just parts (e.g. a logo or pattern). Registration stops other people copying your work for up to 25 years — and it applies throughout the EU.

Inventive step — the new dance routine...

You'd be pretty disappointed if you'd come up with a fantastic idea and then someone nicked it right from under your nose. Well, it's a good thing that there are plenty of ways of protecting designs.

Presenting and Protecting Design Ideas

Once designers are completely satisfied with a design, they have to <u>present</u> the idea to the <u>client</u>. The client can then decide whether it's what they want.

You Need to *Present* Your *Final Design*

It's important to present your design clearly and with as big an impact as possible.
The best way to do this is with really good presentation drawings — they help the <u>client</u> (or in your case, the examiner) to clearly <u>visualise</u> the product.

1) You should ideally have <u>two different</u> types of presentation drawing:

- A <u>3D rendered drawing</u> showing how the finished product will look (see p. 20). This could include pictures of the product <u>in use</u> or in its environment.
- A <u>working drawing</u> with dimensions (see p. 19) and other details, e.g. materials and finishes (see section 4). The client will probably want to see this one too — and the <u>manufacturer</u> definitely needs it. <u>Exploded views</u> can help to show how complicated parts work (see p. 18).

2) Presentation drawings can be done using <u>CAD</u> (see pages 19 and 23). You can make 3D drawings look very <u>realistic</u> by adding texture and light effects. And if you do <u>working drawings</u> in CAD, they'll be very <u>neat</u> and <u>accurate</u>.

3) Neat, <u>hand-drawn</u> presentation drawings are also fine. The downside of doing this in industry is that the designer would have to <u>re-draw</u> it if the client wanted them to make any <u>alterations</u>.

You could include a really short description of the product and its best features to help explain the drawings.

EXAM TIP
You'll probably have to do a final presentation drawing in your exam — make sure it's <u>really neat</u> and uses colour and shading.

Once the client has given the design the thumbs up, you need to think about <u>advertising</u> the product to potential customers. You can create advertisements using ICT and CAD — and there are plenty of effects you can use to make the product look <u>appealing</u> (see p. 22-23).

Practice Questions

1) a) What is meant by a <u>trademark</u>?
   b) How can you tell that something has been <u>trademarked</u>?
   c) Give two <u>famous</u> trademarks.

2) a) What are <u>patents</u> used for?
   b) Why would a patent not be given to someone who has designed a <u>box</u> made of cardboard?

3) David has had an idea for a new way to build conservatories.
   a) How could David <u>protect</u> his idea?
   b) If a building company wanted to <u>use his idea</u> what would they have to do?

4) Joe works for a large lawnmower firm. He comes up with a new design of lawnmower. Who owns the <u>copyright</u> for his idea?

5) Ruby has designed a new vacuum cleaner. How would Ruby benefit from <u>registering the design</u> of her vacuum cleaner?

6) You have designed a new pair of trainers and have to present your ideas to a client. Explain how you could use <u>CAD</u> to help.

Working Schedules and Quality Control

Quality assurance (QA) is the systems and procedures that manufacturers have in place to make sure that their products are high quality.

Manufacturers Want Customer Satisfaction

If you just think about design as what you do in D&T lessons, you might see evaluation as the end of the design process. In industry, the end of the process is customer satisfaction...

See page 10 for more on evaluation.

> Customer satisfaction is achieved when the product works, is great to use, and is good value for money.

The way to make this happen is to make sure your product is high quality. You can also use customer feedback (what users of the product think) to check whether your customers are satisfied. Oh, and make sure your product is safe (see p. 62-63) — an injured customer is not a happy customer.

Quality Assurance is an Overall System

1) Top companies that do QA well are awarded ISO 9000 — an international standard of quality management.

2) QA includes having good staff training, procedures for checking the quality of materials and systems for keeping machinery maintained.

3) It also includes quality control checks throughout the manufacturing process — see below.

4) So when you're planning a manufacturing process (for your project or in the exam) remember to work in quality checks at every stage.

The aim of all this is to ensure that products:

> 1) do the job they were designed to do
> 2) meet the standards set down by the relevant institutions
>   E.g. the British Standards Institution or the British Electrotechnical Approvals Board.
> 3) keep the customer happy
> 4) are manufactured consistently
>   Using templates and jigs (see page 84) and CAD/CAM helps to make sure that products are consistent. This is particularly important in batch production.

Quality Control Means Checking Components

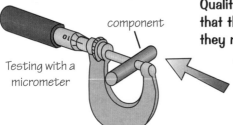

component

Testing with a micrometer

Quality control means testing samples of components to check that they meet the manufacturer's specification. For example, they must be the right colour and the right size.

When components are checked for size they must be within a specific tolerance. Tolerance is given as an upper (+) and lower (−) limit for the measurement. For example, if a component should have a diameter of 20 mm (±0.5), then a micrometer reading of 19.9 mm would be OK but 20.7 mm would not.

Tolerance — needed when you've got revision to do...

I guess customer satisfaction would be buying this book but not having to spend hours revising from it. Sorry, but if you want to give high quality answers in the exam you need to do high quality revision.

Working Schedules and Quality Control

Designers don't normally <u>make</u> stuff — but they do have to <u>tell the manufacturer</u> how to make the product.

You Need to Produce a Manufacturing Plan

1) The designer produces <u>working drawings</u> that show the manufacturer exactly what the product is like. These could be <u>assembly drawings</u> (page 18) or <u>3rd angle orthographic projections</u> (page 19). Whatever type, they should include:
   - <u>materials</u> — which materials to use for each part and how much will be needed,
   - <u>sizes</u> — <u>precise measurements</u> of each part in <u>millimetres</u>,
   - <u>tolerances</u> — the maximum and minimum sizes each part should be.

2) The <u>manufacturer</u> then draws up a <u>production plan</u> for how to make the product.

3) Production plans say what <u>order</u> to do things in and <u>how long</u> each stage should take. They should also have <u>quality control checks</u> built in.

Flow charts show work order

You need to plan <u>in sequence</u> each task to be carried out, including quality control checks. For example:

Gather materials → Print design onto card → Cut out nets → Are nets and print accurate? — Yes → Fold boxes

No

<u>Start</u> and <u>end</u> a flow chart with a sausage-shaped box.

<u>Processes</u> go in rectangular boxes.

If the product or component doesn't look and work how it should, <u>go back</u> and make sure it's done properly before you move on.

<u>Decisions</u> go in diamond-shaped boxes. These let you show <u>quality control checks</u>.

Gantt charts show timings

You also need to work out <u>how long</u> each stage will take, and how these times will fit into the <u>total time</u> you've allowed for production.

The tasks are down the <u>left-hand</u> side, and the <u>time</u> is plotted across the top. The coloured squares show <u>how long</u> each task takes, and the <u>order</u> they're done in.

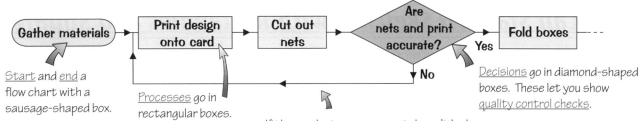

You can start the next stage while the paint's drying, so draw the bars underneath each other.

Practice Questions

1) a) Why might a firm be awarded <u>ISO 9000</u>?
   b) What is meant by <u>quality control</u>?

2 Suggest a suitable tolerance for a frying pan handle that should be <u>250 mm</u> long.

3) Mike is making a table. He has made a <u>Gantt chart</u> of the process.
   a) Why do some of the bars <u>overlap</u>?
   b) How long does the <u>whole process</u> last?
   c) Which is the <u>longest</u> stage? How long does it last?

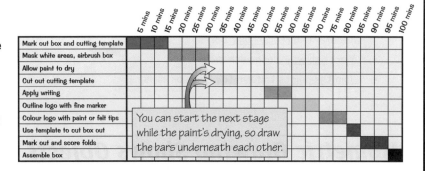

Drawing Techniques

You don't always have to use <u>perfect drawings</u>. <u>Freehand</u> sketches are fine for getting across <u>initial ideas</u>. And they're much easier to do, so you can get new thoughts on paper quickly.

Develop Ideas <u>with Sketches</u>

1) 'Freehand' means drawing <u>without using any equipment</u> (except a pencil or pen).

2) You can <u>combine</u> <u>2D</u> and <u>3D</u> sketches to explain details.

3) And you can <u>annotate</u> your sketches (add <u>notes</u>) to explain details further, e.g. describing the <u>materials</u> and <u>processes</u> you'd use.

<u>You Can Start 2D Sketches with</u> <u>Rectangles</u> <u>and</u> <u>Squares</u>

One way of making your sketches more <u>accurate</u> is to start by <u>ruling guidelines</u>.

1) Using <u>vertical</u> and <u>horizontal</u> lines you can create squares and rectangles.

2) Use these to draw the <u>outline</u> of your shape first.

3) Details can be added by drawing more <u>squares</u> and <u>rectangles</u>.

4) Add <u>circles</u> and <u>ellipses</u> where necessary.

- <u>Circles</u> are drawn in <u>square</u> boxes and <u>ellipses</u> are drawn in <u>rectangular</u> boxes.
- Mark <u>half way</u> along each side.
- <u>Join the points</u> to form the circle or ellipse.

<u>Isometric Drawing</u> <u>Shows Objects at 30°</u>

1) Isometric drawing can be used to show a <u>3D picture</u> of an object.

2) It <u>doesn't show perspective</u> (things don't get smaller in the distance), but it's <u>easy to get dimensions</u> right.

3) There are <u>three main rules</u> when drawing in isometric:

> - Vertical edges are drawn as vertical lines.
> - Horizontal edges are drawn at 30°.
> - Parallel edges appear as parallel lines.

This drawing's been done on isometric <u>dot paper</u>. You could use plain paper and a <u>30°/60° set square</u> instead.

<u>If you've got a freehand could you just help me with this...</u>

There are some pretty nifty drawing techniques on these pages — particularly the ways to draw circles and ellipses by starting with a box. Try to use a range of these techniques when you're designing.

Drawing Techniques

Crating Can Be Used to Draw 3D Shapes

Crating is where you start by drawing a box — the 'crate' — and gradually add bits on and take bits off till you get the right shape. For example, you can remove sections from a cuboid to make any other 3D shape.

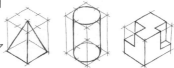

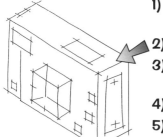

1) When you're sketching a 3D object, it's easier if you imagine it as a basic shape.

2) First draw the basic geometric shape faintly.

3) Stick to a particular drawing technique — isometric drawing, for example.

4) The object can then be drawn within the box.

5) Details of the object can be added by drawing more geometric shapes on top.

Wireframe Drawings Aren't Shaded

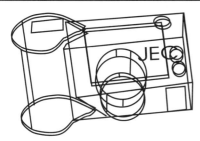

1) When you draw using the crating technique, you can leave the solid sides of the shape unshaded.

2) Doing this lets you see straight through the object — it's called wireframe.

3) This could be used to show details on all faces of an object.

4) You can also view an object in wireframe in CAD software, like the camera shown here.

Practice Questions

1) a) What is freehand drawing?
   b) Suggest what you'd use it for.
   c) Why is it a good idea to annotate freehand sketches?

2) Draw an ellipse 4 cm wide and 7 cm long using guidelines.

3) Bob is doing an isometric drawing.
   At what angle should he draw the horizontal edges of the object?

4) a) What is crating?
   b) Draw a design for a radio using crating.
   c) What type of drawing does crating produce if the solid sides of the shape are left unshaded?

5) Fred wants to advertise his new board game with a picture of a dice.
   a) What kind of drawing should he use to show three sides of the dice with the right dimensions?
   b) Draw a dice using the technique named in part a).

Drawing Techniques

3D drawing techniques can be really useful when doing the final <u>presentation drawings</u> (see page 13) for the client and the manufacturer. They're great for showing products from a variety of <u>angles</u>.

Perspective Drawing <u>Uses</u> Vanishing Points

1) <u>Perspective drawing</u> tries to show what something actually looks like — smaller in the distance, larger close to. It does this by using lines that appear to meet at points called <u>vanishing points</u>.

2) These points are in the distance on the <u>horizon line</u>.

One-Point Perspective — for drawing objects head on.
1) Mark <u>one vanishing point</u>.
2) Draw the <u>front</u> view of the object <u>head on</u>.
3) Then draw <u>lines</u> to the <u>vanishing point</u>.

vanishing point

EXAM TIP
<u>Practise</u> the techniques on these two pages — you'll have to use them for the <u>design question</u> in the exam.

Two-Point Perspective — for drawing objects at an angle.
1) Draw a <u>horizon</u> line <u>horizontally</u> across the page.
2) Mark <u>two vanishing points</u> on the horizon line.
3) Draw the object by starting with the front, vertical edge and then <u>projecting lines</u> to the vanishing points.
4) Remember that <u>vertical lines remain vertical</u> and all <u>horizontal lines go to the vanishing points</u>.

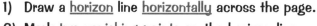

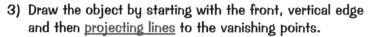

Assembly Drawings <u>Show How Things</u> Fit Together

<u>Exploded views</u> and <u>sectional drawings</u> are two types of assembly drawing.

Exploded views
1) You draw the product with <u>each separate part</u> of it <u>moved out</u> as if it's been exploded.
2) Each part of the product is <u>drawn in line</u> with the part it's attached to.
3) Dotted lines show where the part has been <u>exploded from</u>.
4) They're often used for <u>flat-pack furniture</u> instructions.

This exploded view is also an isometric drawing.

Sectional drawings show what the product would look like inside if you cut it in two.
In this diagram the product is imagined to be <u>cut in half</u> through section X,Y.

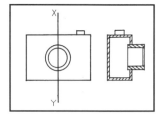

Plan Views <u>Should be Drawn to Scale</u>

1) Plan views are drawn from <u>above</u>.
2) The <u>scale</u> must be shown clearly as a <u>ratio</u>, e.g. **1:2**. With a scale of <u>1:2</u> the drawing is <u>half</u> the product's <u>actual size</u>. (And of course <u>1:1</u> is <u>full size</u>.)
3) Plan views are used in the <u>building industry</u> by architects and planners, to map out rooms, furniture and installations.

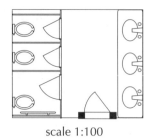
scale 1:100

Exploded views — bits of mine have gone everywhere...

Get a bit of <u>practice</u> by drawing some things using these techniques. For example, try drawing exploded views of some products around your house and have a go at drawing a plan view of your bedroom.

Drawing Techniques

Orthographic Projection *Shows* 2D Views *of a 3D Object*

1) The symbol for 3rd angle orthographic projection is:

2) The front view, plan view and end view of the product are drawn accurately to scale.

3) Dimensions are always given in millimetres.

4) To avoid confusion, lines and dimensions must conform to the following British Standards recommendations:

   ―――――   outlines: thick and continuous

   ─────   projection/construction lines: light and continuous

   ‐·‐·‐·‐   centre lines: alternate short and long dashes, light

   ---------   hidden details: short dashes, light

   ◄―34―►   dimension lines: medium and continuous, with solid arrowheads and the dimension written above the line in the middle (or to the left of the line if it's angled or vertical)

5) There's always a gap between the projection lines and the object.

6) The diameter of a circle is shown by the symbol ∅ and an arrow inside the circle.

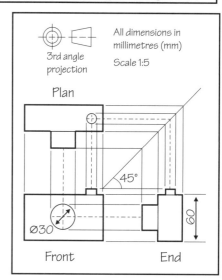

3rd angle projection of camera

CAD *is* Computer Aided Design

1) CAD (Computer Aided Design) can be very useful when you're developing your ideas.

2) CAD software ranges from 2D drawing programs (e.g. TechSoft 2D DESIGN) to 3D modelling packages (e.g. Pro/ENGINEER®, SolidWorks®).

3) CAD helps designers model and change their designs quickly. It's easy to experiment with different colours and shapes and you can spot problems before making anything.

4) In 3D programs, you can view a design from all angles, explode parts and look inside, and even animate components (make them move) to simulate what would happen when the product is used.

5) Another advantage is that you can do rapid prototyping (see p. 83) of your design using CAD/CAM.

CAD/CAM systems work by using x, y, z coordinates. The CAD software works out the coordinates of each point on your drawing — x is the left/right position, y is forwards/backwards and z is up/down. A CAM machine can follow these coordinates and move the tools to cut out (or build up) your design.

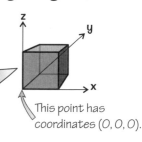

This point has coordinates (0, 0, 0).

Practice Questions

1) What is a vanishing point?

2) A company wants you to design a point-of-sale display for their new chocolate bar.
   a) Sketch the outline of a chocolate bar using one-point perspective.
   b) Now draw it above the horizon line using two-point perspective.

3) What are the three views you need to draw when doing a 3rd angle orthographic projection of an object?

4) a) Suggest a type of drawing that is suitable for flat-pack furniture instructions.
   b) Explain why this type of drawing is suitable.

5) a) What kind of drawing shows you the internal details of an object?
   b) Draw this washing machine as if you were looking at it cut in two through section X,Y.

Drawing Enhancements

There are plenty of things you can do to make your drawings look <u>realistic</u>.

Pencil Shading Can Make Drawings Look 3D

<u>Shading</u> can be added to a shape to make it look <u>3D</u>.

1) Shading a drawing to show <u>depth</u>, <u>light and shade</u> or <u>texture</u> is called <u>rendering</u>.
2) Different <u>pencils</u> can be used to create different <u>tones</u>.
3) A <u>soft pencil</u> will create a <u>wider range of tones</u>.
4) Think about where the light's coming from —
make areas <u>furthest</u> from the light the <u>darkest</u>.

LIGHT

LIGHT

There are Different Ways to Shade With a Pencil

Using different types of shading is useful for showing the different <u>surfaces</u> and <u>parts</u> of an object.

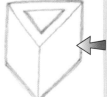

If you can see <u>both surfaces</u> that form a line, draw a <u>thin</u> line. If you can only see <u>one surface</u>, draw a <u>thick line</u>. This gives the impression that the shape is <u>solid</u>.

<u>Highlights</u> are used to suggest <u>reflections</u>. They can be created by leaving <u>white</u> areas.

You can shade using <u>dots</u> — just use a <u>different concentration of dots</u> on each side. Some printers use this method, but it's fairly <u>time-consuming</u> by hand.

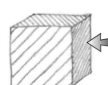

You can also shade using <u>lines</u>. You need to use <u>lines at different spacing</u> on each side. Lines at <u>different angles</u> can be used to show different colours, materials, etc.

Inks, Paints, Pastels, Felt Pens and Markers — Ace

For drawing lines you can use:

1) <u>Fine-liners</u> — which come in a variety of thicknesses and colours. They're <u>great</u> for drawing fine, precise lines and <u>outlining drawings</u>, e.g. orthographic drawings.
2) <u>Markers</u> — they're great for thicker lines. You can get markers in hundreds of different colours and with different tips (<u>chisel</u>, <u>bullet</u> and <u>brush</u>).

For filling areas of colour you can use:

1) <u>Inks</u> — which are pigments suspended in water or another solvent. They're good for <u>colour infilling</u>, <u>background washes</u> and <u>writing</u>.
2) <u>Chalk pastels</u> — great for <u>backgrounds</u> or to add <u>tone and shading</u>. They're easily <u>blended</u> using your fingers or cotton wool.
3) <u>Gouache</u> — an <u>opaque paint</u> (not see-through). You can use it for <u>flat areas of colour</u>, or <u>highlights</u> on renderings.

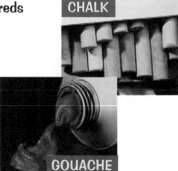

CHALK

GOUACHE

Keep out of the sun — do some shading...

It's a good idea to practise some of these shading techniques before doing them for real in your project or the exam. It'll keep the moderators and examiners happy if you can use a variety of methods.

Drawing Enhancements

Colours Can be Organised into Different Groups

There are two main groups of colours — primary and secondary.

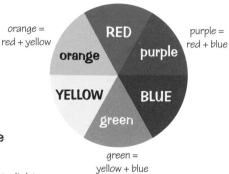

orange = red + yellow

purple = red + blue

green = yellow + blue

1) The primary colours — red , blue and yellow — can be mixed together to produce many other colours.

2) Secondary colours — orange , purple and green — are colours made by mixing together primary colours. For example, orange is made by mixing together yellow and red.

3) Colour can be represented on a colour wheel which shows you how all the colours fit together. The secondary colours are made by mixing the primary colours on either side of them.

This colour wheel only applies to paint or pigments — not to light.
(The primary colours for light are red, green and blue, which gives a different set of secondary colours too.)

Colours Have Different Hues and Tones

1) Hue is just another word for colour — it's the actual colour (e.g. red, green, orange, etc.).

2) The tone of a colour (how dark or light it is) can be changed by adding black or white to it. For example, blue can have different tones, e.g. light blue, royal blue or navy blue.

more white

Complementary Colours Are Contrasting

1) Complementary colours are found opposite each other on the colour wheel — green and red, purple and yellow and orange and blue.

2) These colours are contrasting — they stand out against each other and can seem more intense than when they're on their own.

EXAM TIP
Think about which colours go together well — you don't want to have to start your drawing again.

In CAD packages you can select and change colours really easily — so it's a good way to experiment with the effect of different colours on the overall look of your design.

Practice Questions

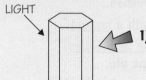

LIGHT

1) Copy the shape on the left.
Use a pencil to shade it to make it look 3D.

2) Copy the cube on the right.
Use thick and thin lines to make it look solid.

3) a) What are the two main groups of colours?
b) How can you change the tone of a colour?
c) Name a colour that will contrast with blue.

Presentation Techniques

There are ways to represent different <u>materials</u>.

For <u>Wood</u> <u>Use</u> <u>Colour</u> <u>and</u> <u>Draw</u> <u>a</u> <u>Grain</u>

1) <u>Wood</u> can be drawn using <u>coloured pencils</u> to represent the <u>colour</u> and <u>grain</u>.

2) You can use more than one colour to get the <u>right shade</u>.

3) <u>Wood grain</u> can be added using a <u>darker</u> pencil. Remember that the <u>side</u> grain and the <u>end</u> grain look <u>different</u>.

There Are a Few Tricks for <u>Plastic</u>

1) <u>Marker pens</u> can be used to create the look of <u>plastic</u>. Alternatively you could use soft <u>coloured pencils</u> or <u>poster paints</u>. Adding <u>white lines</u> to a surface can make the object look <u>reflective</u>.

2) <u>Pale</u> coloured <u>marker pens</u>, <u>watercolour paints or pencils</u> or <u>coloured pencils</u> can be used to make an object appear <u>transparent</u>. You may even see objects through the transparent object.

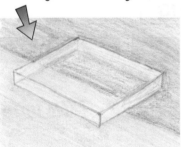

3) Most <u>dark</u> colours look opaque automatically, but you could make a <u>pale</u> coloured material look <u>opaque</u> using <u>watercolour paints</u> by adding a bit of yellow.

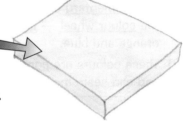

Draw the <u>Reflections</u> <u>if Metal</u> <u>is</u> <u>Shiny</u>

1) <u>Metals</u> can have a variety of colours and finishes.

2) You could have flat <u>sheet metal</u>, or metal with a <u>texture</u>.

3) <u>Textured metal</u> can be represented using <u>line techniques</u>, e.g. drawing lines to show any ridges, bumps etc.

4) When shading <u>shiny metal</u> you must be aware of <u>highlights</u>. Try looking closely at a piece of shiny metal in the light and thinking about what the <u>reflections</u> actually look like.

Watch out for splinters — oh, it's not real...

These techniques will help to make your sketches look more realistic. If you use them in your final <u>presentation drawings</u> (page 13) you'll be able to give a good idea of what your product will look like.

Presentation Techniques

Design Drawings Can Be Edited Using CAD

Using CAD packages (e.g. SolidWorks®) you can produce and edit drawings
of a product. The images can be manipulated in a number of ways:

1) You can alter colours easily and add special light and shadow effects, e.g. to make metal look like it's gleaming.

2) You can show details of dimensions and materials.

3) Doing simple things like changing the background can make a big difference — make the most of using computer effects to make your presentation drawing stand out.

Some Software Can Be Used to Manipulate Photos

If you use a digital camera to take photos, the images can easily be stored on a
computer and used in presentations and reports. Computer software can then be
used to manipulate the photographs, e.g. Paint Shop Pro and Adobe® Photoshop®.

1) Colours can be altered easily. For example, you could manipulate the photo to show how a product would look with different finishes.

2) Special effects can be added. For example, photos can be edited so that they look distorted or to make them look like pencil drawings.

3) These techniques are widely used in products such as posters and leaflets, and on websites.

Digital cameras are also useful for when you're making a mood board (p. 9).
You can zoom in on different materials to show the texture and finish.

Practice Questions

1) Suggest what techniques and equipment you'd use to draw a block of wood.

2) a) Suggest two pieces of drawing equipment you could use to create the look of plastic.
   b) Suggest a way of making a pale-coloured material look opaque.

3) What technique could you use to show the reflections in metal?

4) a) Name a CAD package that you might use to create a design.
   b) Give two ways that you can change the presentation of a design using CAD.

5) Hayley has taken a photo of her finished product.
   She wants to use the photo to make a poster to advertise the product.
   a) Name a software package that she could use to manipulate the photo.
   b) Suggest a special effect she could use.
   c) Suggest another way she could manipulate the photo.

Packaging and the Environment

Most products come in <u>packaging</u> and it's not just there to make the product look nice. Read and enjoy...

Products are Packaged in Different Materials

A variety of materials are used to make packaging. For example:

1) <u>Paper</u> and <u>card</u> — used to make bags and boxes.
2) <u>Textiles</u> — used to make bags.
3) <u>Metals</u>, e.g. aluminium and steel — used to make cans and foil trays.
4) <u>Plastic</u>, e.g. polystyrene, PVC, etc. — used to make bottles, tubs, trays, bags, boxes, bubble wrap and air pillows (small plastic pillows filled with air).
5) <u>Glass</u> — used to make bottles, jars, etc.

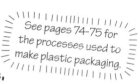
See pages 74-75 for the processes used to make plastic packaging.

Packaging has Several Functions

Packaging is used to <u>contain</u> and store products, to <u>protect</u> them — particularly during <u>transport</u> — and to <u>preserve</u> the contents.

Packaging is also used to <u>inform</u> consumers about the product (see p. 26-27) and to <u>display</u> the product (see p. 29)

Containment and Storage

1) Many products need packaging to <u>contain</u> them. It would be difficult to buy, say, a board game, if all the pieces weren't held together in one package...
2) Packaging also makes it easier to store products — well designed packaging makes things <u>fit neatly together</u> side-by-side.
3) Products are often stored <u>on top</u> of each other — so the packaging has to be strong enough not to <u>collapse</u> under the weight of other objects.

Protection

1) When products are <u>transported</u>, they need to be protected to stop them being <u>broken</u>.
2) Packaging materials like <u>cardboard</u>, <u>bubble wrap</u>, <u>air pillows</u> and <u>expanded polystyrene</u> can protect a product from knocks.
3) Packaging is also used for the <u>security</u> of the product it contains.
4) Electrical equipment such as DVDs, games, cameras, etc. often have <u>anti-theft devices</u> inserted into the packaging — this sets off an alarm if anyone tries to steal them.
5) Some security devices are filled with <u>ink</u> — if you try to take them off without the proper machine, they break open and the item is <u>ruined</u>.
6) Many food products have <u>tamper-evident seals</u> to show whether they've been <u>opened</u>.

Preservation

1) Many products (especially <u>food</u>) begin to <u>deteriorate</u> when they're exposed to <u>oxygen</u> in the air.
2) Sealed <u>glass jars</u> and <u>bottles</u>, <u>'tin' cans</u> and <u>tubes</u> are used as <u>airtight</u> packaging for food and drink, and other products, e.g. toothpaste.
3) However, <u>plastics</u> and <u>composite materials</u> (e.g. card and aluminium foil laminated together) are now widely used.

Packaging — so good I can barely contain my excitement...

OK, OK, packaging isn't that thrilling, but it is <u>important</u>. There's a whole load of things that I wouldn't fancy buying without it. Frozen peas for example. Or ink. Shampoo would also be tricky. And jam...

Packaging and the Environment

Packaging has an Environmental Impact

1) Producing packaging for products uses up <u>materials</u>. For example, packaging is often made of <u>plastic</u>. Most plastic is made using <u>crude oil</u>, which is a <u>finite resource</u> (it'll run out eventually).

2) It's not just materials — the <u>processes</u> used to make packaging also have an impact. For example, moulding plastic uses <u>energy</u>. Most of this energy comes from burning fossil fuels — which causes air pollution and emits carbon dioxide, which contributes to <u>global warming</u>.

3) Packaging also produces <u>waste</u> — and it's mostly disposed of in <u>landfill</u> once it's removed from the product. If the packaging is made from non-biodegradable materials it'll be there for centuries.

The Environmental Impact Can Be Limited

Many people think that manufacturers and consumers have a social responsibility to <u>minimise</u> the environmental impact of using packaging. There are several ways to do this:

<u>REDUCE</u> the amount of packaging — it's a good idea to <u>avoid unnecessary packaging</u>, e.g. by selling chocolates in a <u>paper bag</u> rather than in a plastic tray in a cardboard box wrapped in cellophane. However, manufacturers still have to make sure that items are <u>protected</u> and <u>preserved</u> or else products might <u>break</u> or <u>go off</u>, which is just as wasteful.

<u>RE-USE</u> packaging — this reduces the amount of <u>new</u> packaging that has to be made. For example, printer cartridges can be returned for refilling. However, re-using can have an environmental impact if products need <u>transporting</u> and <u>cleaning</u> first.

<u>USE SUSTAINABLE MATERIALS</u> — for example, <u>corn starch</u> can be used instead of <u>polystyrene</u>. Corn starch packaging is more sustainable because it's made from a <u>renewable resource</u> (sweetcorn) and is <u>biodegradable</u>.

<u>RECYCLE</u> packaging — old packaging can be used to make the same or different products, so <u>less resources</u> are used up. For example, plastic bottles can be recycled into textiles (fleece).

<u>USE RECYCLED MATERIALS</u> — this <u>saves resources</u>, e.g. if you use recycled paper then trees won't have be cut down to make new paper. However, it can be more <u>expensive</u> to use recycled materials than new ones (some plastics are very expensive to recycle, for example).

Practice Questions

1) Name three types of material that you could use to make <u>bags</u>.

2) Alan sells T-shirts and souvenirs by the seaside.
   a) Suggest what packaging he might use to wrap up glass <u>ornaments</u>, and explain your choice.
   b) Why might he attach <u>tags</u> filled with ink to the T-shirts?

3) a) What <u>raw material</u> is used to make most <u>plastic</u> packaging?
   b) Name one <u>alternative</u> material that can be used instead of plastic, and describe its benefits.

4) Briefly describe <u>two</u> environmental impacts of the increased use of packaging.

5) Many supermarkets give customers free <u>carrier bags</u> for their shopping.
   Outline <u>three</u> ways in which a supermarket could <u>minimise</u> the environmental impact this has.

Labelling

Packaging can be used to <u>inform</u> consumers about the product. This is done through <u>labelling</u>.

Manufacturers Must Label Their Products Carefully

1) Manufacturers <u>must</u> put certain information on packaging by <u>law</u> — the information they have to provide varies depending on what the product is.

2) It's the manufacturer's responsibility to make sure that information on the label is <u>accurate</u>.

3) If labelling is wrong or misleading, the manufacturers could be breaking laws or regulations, e.g. the <u>Consumer Protection from Unfair Trading Regulations</u>.

Labels Give Information About Product Safety...

1) Some products are <u>hazardous</u> to people and/or the environment. They must have <u>hazard symbols</u> displayed on their labels. For example...

Harmful

Flammable

Explosive

Irritant

Environmental Hazard

EXAM TIP
You're expected to know these hazard symbols.

For example, a lot of <u>paints</u> and <u>solvents</u> give off harmful fumes.

2) Products may be labelled to show that they've met certain <u>standards</u> for safety or <u>quality of design</u>. These standards are set by different organisations, depending on the type of product.

The <u>British Standards Institution (BSI)</u> is one example. Products which meet its standards are awarded the Kitemark — manufacturers can put this on their label (many plastic products have it <u>moulded</u> on).

 Certain types of product must also meet <u>EU standards</u> for safety, shown by the '<u>CE</u>' mark, before they can be sold in Europe.

3) If a company's products meet the standards they might be more profitable — many consumers are more willing to buy '<u>approved</u>' products, or will <u>pay more</u> for them.

...and Whether Designs are Protected

Designers usually take steps to <u>protect</u> their work from being copied.

1) Products labelled with the © symbol are protected under <u>copyright law</u>. This stops other people from copying <u>written</u>, <u>drawn</u> and <u>recorded</u> work, e.g. books, comics, art and music.

2) <u>Symbols</u>, <u>logos</u>, <u>words</u> or <u>slogans</u> followed by a ™ mark or an ®, e.g. Google™, are <u>trademarks</u>. Trademarks are used to represent companies and can't be copied by other companies.

Revision — definitely an irritant, possibly harmful...

We're told to <u>always read the label</u> and it turns out there are good reasons for this. Not reading it can lead to shrunken clothes, badly dyed hair and (in the worst cases) serious <u>safety</u> issues. Not good.

Labelling

Labels Also Have Use and Disposal Information

1) Manufacturers use labels to inform consumers about the product.

For example, this novelty sticky-tape holder has a label telling you how to:

THIS IS NOT A TOY, CONTENTS NOT FIT FOR CONSUMPTION. → use the product,
IF CONTACT WITH OIL OCCURS, WASH WITH SOAP & WATER. → maintain it,
DO NOT LEAVE IN DIRECT SUNLIGHT AS LIQUID MAY DISCOLOUR. → and store it.
NOT SUITABLE FOR CHILDREN UNDER 6 YEARS.
CONTAINS SMALL PARTS WHICH COULD REPRESENT A CHOKING HAZARD → It also gives specific safety information.

2) Labels may also give information about how to dispose of the product or packaging. For example:

This symbol shows that the packaging is made from recyclable aluminium...

...this one shows it can be recycled at cardboard recyclers...

...and the Wheelie Bin symbol shows the product is electrical or electronic equipment and should be disposed of at a suitable collection site.

3) Plastic packaging usually has a symbol showing what type of plastic it is.

These symbols help recycling stations to sort the plastics. For example: This symbol means it's PVC.   This symbol is found on polystyrene products, e.g. foam cups and protective packaging.

Food Packaging Has Lots of Symbols

MED Saturated fat 2.4 g per serving
LOW Salt 0.2 g per serving
HIGH Sugar 41.1 g per serving

1) Symbols are used to show that food is suitable for a particular diet, e.g. food suitable for vegetarians is often shown with a green V.

2) Possible allergy problems can be highlighted, e.g. 'may contain traces of nuts'.

3) Traffic-light labelling on a product shows how healthy it is at a glance. Red, orange and green colours show whether a product has high, medium or low amounts of saturated fat, salt and sugar. For example, a pizza might be red for saturated fat and yellow for salt and sugar.

Practice Questions

1) a) What symbol might you see on a product that has met BSI quality standards?
   b) What does the CE symbol mean?
   c) Why might it benefit a company to have these symbols on their product?

2) GiantzComics™ make comic books.
   a) Why aren't people allowed to copy pictures from the comic and use them?
   b) Why couldn't a new company open up and call themselves GiantzComics™?

3) a) Suggest three types of information you might find on the label of some hair straighteners.
   b) Design a label for the hair straighteners, including all the information you suggested in a).

Section 3 — Packaging and Marketing

Brands and Marketing

Packaging can be part of a company's <u>marketing</u>. (Marketing is all the things a company does to persuade consumers to <u>buy</u> a product.) Marketing strategies also include <u>branding</u> and <u>advertising</u>.

Marketing Should be Aimed at a Target Group

It's important to <u>understand</u> the group of people you want to sell your product to — the <u>target market</u>. The <u>marketing strategy</u> needs to be aimed at this group. You can group people by things like <u>age</u>, <u>gender</u>, <u>job</u>, <u>hobbies</u> and <u>how wealthy</u> they are.

> For example, the target market for <u>pop-up recipe books</u> is probably the <u>relatives</u> of <u>young children</u> who are interested in cooking, so you might advertise the recipe books on a website that sells gifts for children.

Branding is an Important Part of Promotion...

Most companies want people to <u>recognise their products</u> and <u>feel positive</u> about the company.

1) <u>Memorable graphics</u> are a really good way to make sure that consumers <u>recognise</u> the product, e.g. using a <u>logo</u>. Many companies apply their logo and colour scheme to all <u>printed material</u> (e.g. business cards, letterheads and compliments slips) as well as their <u>products</u>, <u>packaging</u>, <u>uniforms</u> and <u>transport</u>.

2) <u>Well-designed</u> graphics that are appropriate to the target market should help the company to <u>get its message across</u> and build up its <u>brand image</u> — the image it wants people to have of the company or product.

For example, a company aiming products at young people might want to develop a brand image that's modern and creative. They would use very different <u>colours</u> and <u>typefaces</u> from a company whose brand image was all about classic styles aimed at an older age group.

EXAM TIP
You might have to suggest ways to promote a certain product.

3) Companies like McDonald's and NIKE have <u>strong brands</u>. Most people know what the company does and can recognise it from its logo alone, <u>without the need for words</u>. This is great for the company.

Get this stuff branded onto your brain...

So, first off, decide who your product is <u>for</u>. Then <u>market</u> it in a way that will <u>appeal</u> to them, in a place where they'll <u>see</u> it. If all goes well they'll get sucked in and <u>buy</u> loads, leaving you filthy rich. Excellent.

Brands and Marketing

...and so is Advertising

1) There are loads and loads of places that products can be advertised. For example:

- Television, cinema and radio adverts can be used to target specific groups, e.g. advertising toys between children's TV programs. Some TV adverts (ones with good catchphrases, say) become talking points.

- Paper advertising, e.g. magazines, newspapers, leaflets and flyers can also be targeted, e.g. advertising clothes in fashion magazines.

- Internet adverts, e.g. pop-ups and emails, reach a wide audience and are quite cheap, but can annoy people.

- Billboards and adverts on trains, buses, etc. are seen regularly by large numbers of people, e.g. as they travel to work each day. So loads of potential consumers are constantly exposed to the product but the advertising is not very targeted.

2) Companies can sponsor teams or events, e.g. sports teams often have their sponsor's logo on their shirts. Sponsorship can help to develop a company's brand image, e.g. sponsoring a charity event might create a caring, responsible image.

3) Paying a celebrity to say how great your product is can encourage people to buy it — as long as you choose someone who reflects the image you want to project. Consumers are also more likely to be persuaded by celebrities who have expertise in the product area, e.g. a chef advertising food products.

A Good Display Helps to Sell Products

1) The packaging is an important part of product display — it should make it clear what the product is (e.g. by using transparent windows), and should also be attractive to entice people to buy it.

2) Packaging should help to make the product stand out — bright colours or a large logo can help.

3) The product can also be promoted inside the shop (point of sale promotion) either by the retailer or the manufacturer. Point of sale promotions include signs that stick out into the shop aisle or hang above the product — attracting customers' attention.

4) Other promotion tactics include offering free samples (e.g. of food or perfume) or in-shop demonstrations (e.g. of toys and tools).

Practice Questions

1) A car manufacturer has brought out a new model of a convertible sports car.
   a) Suggest who their target market might be.
   b) Where might they advertise their new car?

2) a) Why do some businesses have a logo?
   b) Fast food retailers often have their logo on their shopfronts.
      Suggest two other places they might put the logo.
   c) Explain how a logo could help a business appeal to young people?

3) a) Suggest a place where a sports company might advertise their new trainers.
   b) Give two benefits of advertising on the internet.

4) A firm is making a new brand of baked beans.
   Describe two ways in which they could promote their beans in shops.

Properties of Materials

Different Materials Have Different Properties

Make sure you're really familiar with all these terms — if you start getting strength and hardness mixed up, or get confused between malleable and ductile, you'll be dropping marks all over the place.

STRENGTH

Strength is the ability to withstand forces without breaking. For example:

1) The rope in a tug-of-war resists pulling forces.
2) Bridge supports resist squashing forces.
3) A surfboard resists forces trying to bend it.
4) A rivet resists strong sliding forces.
5) A drill bit resists twisting forces.

HARDNESS

1) This is the ability to withstand scratching, rubbing or denting.
2) It's very important for tools that cut, like files and drills.

PLASTICITY

1) If a material can change shape permanently, without breaking or cracking, it's said to have good plastic qualities.
2) This could mean that the material is malleable (can be moulded, e.g. by hammering) or ductile (can be drawn into wires).

BRITTLENESS

1) Brittle materials can't withstand much stretching.
2) Brittle materials are more likely to crack or break than change their shape.
3) Glass is brittle.

TOUGHNESS

1) Tough is the opposite of brittle.
2) If a material is tough, it can absorb impacts without breaking or snapping.
3) Armour and bulletproof vests need to be tough.

EXAM TIP
You get marks for explaining why a particular material is suitable for a product. E.g. 'because it's durable'.

I'm durable.

DURABILITY

1) If a product is durable it's able to withstand repeated use.
2) Durable products also withstand wear and tear and are resistant to corrosion (e.g. they don't rust).

Some live in bungalows, some in semi-detached...

Property jokes aside, you need to be able to say why a material is suitable for a product, and there's only one way you can do that... you really need to get your head around what all these terms mean.

Section 4 — Materials and Components

Properties of Materials

There are Other Factors to Think About Too...

When it comes to choosing which material to use in a product, there's a lot to consider:

FUNCTIONAL REQUIREMENTS

1) What demands will be made on the material? For example, it might have to hold heavy loads.

2) Will it be used outdoors or indoors? You'll need to consider whether your material will corrode.

3) Does it need to fit in with an environment? It might need a certain look.

AVAILABILITY

Can you get the material you want in a suitable form? Most materials are only available in standard forms and sizes — it can be very expensive to get them in other forms. This will have a direct effect on the cost and the method of manufacture.

For example, materials might be available as granules, strips, bars, tubes, rough sawn, planed...

PRODUCTION METHOD

1) Some materials are easier to join than others. *For example, wood can be joined using glue, screws, nails, bolts, knock-down fittings...*

2) The material must be suitable for the intended production method (and vice versa). *For example, you can use injection moulding with plastics but certainly not with wood.*

ECONOMICS

1) You need to think about the size of the product — materials like pewter are expensive, but may be a good choice for a small item of jewellery.

2) Whether your product is a one-off, or will be batch or mass produced (see p. 76-77) will make a difference.

If you're making a one-off, hand-crafted piece of furniture you might use an expensive piece of hardwood. However, if you're mass producing cheap furniture, softwood would probably be fine.

Practice Questions

1) Describe what is meant by the following properties:
   a) brittle   b) malleable   c) ductile

2) Suggest a product that needs to be:
   a) hard   b) durable   c) tough

3) List three products for which strength is an important property, and explain why.

4) The size of a product can affect what material you'd make it from. Explain why.

5) Some products are mass produced and others are one-offs. How might this affect the materials that are used?

6) Cho is designing a slide for a playground. She is deciding whether to make it from plastic or metal.
   a) Suggest the properties that the material needs to have.
   b) Explain why Cho should consider the manufacturing method before choosing a material.
   c) Why does Cho need to think about the shapes of materials available?

Paper and Card

I can tell you want to know more about the <u>materials</u> used to make products. First up, <u>paper</u> and <u>card</u> — pretty useful for <u>writing</u> and <u>sketching</u> (no, really) and also for making products like <u>packaging</u>.

Paper Does Grow on Trees

<u>Trees</u> go through a series of <u>processes</u> before they become <u>paper</u>:

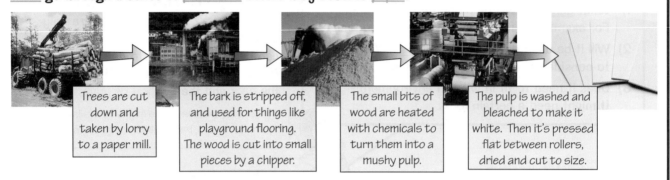

Trees are cut down and taken by lorry to a paper mill.

The bark is stripped off, and used for things like playground flooring. The wood is cut into small pieces by a chipper.

The small bits of wood are heated with chemicals to turn them into a mushy pulp.

The pulp is washed and bleached to make it white. Then it's pressed flat between rollers, dried and cut to size.

There are Different Types of Paper and Card

1) **Cartridge paper** is <u>high quality</u> and has a <u>textured</u> surface, which is great for sketching with pencils, crayons, pastels, gouache, inks and watercolours.

2) **Layout paper** is <u>strong</u>, <u>thin</u> and <u>translucent</u> (you can see light through it) and is used for general design work — particularly sketching ideas.

3) **Grid paper** may have a square or isometric pattern printed on it. Square grid paper's useful for orthographic drawings (see page 19) and isometric paper's good for presentation drawings (see page 13).

square grid paper

isometric grid paper

4) **Tracing paper** is <u>translucent</u>, and is used to <u>copy images</u>.

The weight of paper and board is measured in <u>gsm</u> (grams per square metre). Above <u>200 gsm</u>, it's not paper any more — it's <u>board</u> (also known as <u>card</u>).

1) **Solid white board** has a high quality bleached surface, which is ideal for printing. It's used loads for <u>primary packaging</u> — the packaging directly around the product. (<u>Secondary packaging</u> is an additional layer around the primary packaging — see below.)

2) **Corrugated board** is used a lot in <u>secondary</u> packaging to protect products during transit. It's made up of a <u>fluted inner core</u> sandwiched between <u>two outer layers</u>.

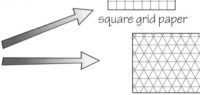

3) **Duplex board** has a <u>different colour</u> and <u>texture</u> on <u>each side</u>. It's often used where only <u>one surface</u> is <u>seen</u>, so that only one side needs to be <u>smooth</u> for <u>printing</u>.

Mmm, paper, my favourite — just add fish and chips...

Paper is pretty sustainable because it's made from a <u>renewable resource</u>. It's even more sustainable if it's <u>recycled</u> — used paper can be turned back into pulp, which is then used to make new paper products.

Paper and Card

You Can Buy Paper in Standard Sizes

1) Paper sizes go from A0 (which has an area of 1 m²) to A1, A2, A3, and so on — halving in size (area) each time.

2) Many other sizes are also available:
   - A4 paper is half the size of A3 paper.
   - A5 paper is half the size of A4 paper.
   - A6 paper is half the size of A5 paper.

   As the paper gets smaller the number increases.

   > The width of A3 paper is the length of A4.
   > The length of A3 paper is double the width of A4.

3) The most common paper sizes used in UK schools are **A4** and **A3**. A4 is 297 mm × 210 mm, in case you're interested.

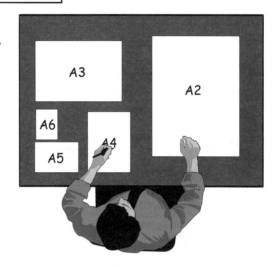

Laminating Paper Gives it New Properties

If you laminate paper by adding a layer of another material, you get a composite with different qualities.

A composite is made up of two or more different materials.

A combination of paper and aluminium foil is often used to package food.

This keeps flavours in and air out, and you can print graphics onto the paper.

Foam core board is made by laminating polystyrene foam between card.

It's stiff but lightweight, and is used for mounting posters and making models.

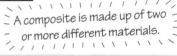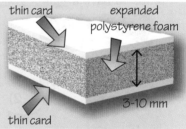

Ernie misunderstood his boss's instruction to build a laminator.

Paper can be coated with polythene to make it waterproof.

Then you can use it for things like paper cups, where normal paper would go soggy pretty quickly.

Practice Questions

1) a) What's the surface of cartridge paper like?
   b) What would you use it for?

2) What properties do layout paper and tracing paper have in common?

3) In what units are the weights of paper and card measured?

4) What is corrugated board often used for?

5) What standard size is this piece of yellow paper? → A2 A?

6) Delia has invented a new mustard, sherry and cheese sauce. She wants to package it in a paper carton.
   a) Suggest what material the paper should be laminated with.
   b) How would adding this material change the properties of the carton?

Timber

I love trees. Not only can you climb them but you can turn them into timber (chunks of solid wood).

Wood is Either Hardwood or Softwood

Wood comes in two sorts — expensive hardwoods and cheaper softwoods.

SOFTWOODS grow in colder climates and are fast growing —
this makes them fairly cheap. The trees have leaves like needles,
are usually evergreen and have cones (e.g. pine, cedar).

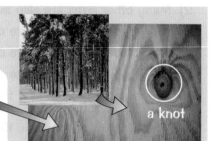
a knot

1) Scots pine is yellow with brown streaks. It's quite strong and cheap — but knotty, which makes it harder to work with. It's used for telegraph poles, fences and cheap furniture.

2) Parana pine is pale yellow with red streaks. It's hard and not very knotty — but it's more expensive. It's used for high-quality joinery like interior doors and stairs.

HARDWOODS usually grow in warm climates and are slow growing —
so they're generally more expensive than softwoods. The trees have
broad, flat leaves and are usually deciduous (e.g. oak, teak). The wood
tends to have a tighter grain and be denser and harder than softwood.

1) Mahogany is a red-brown colour. It's easy to work with but it's expensive, so it's used for good quality furniture.

2) Teak is golden brown. It's hard and weather-resistant, so it's used for garden furniture and window frames, but it's expensive.

3) Ash has a pale cream colour. It's tough and flexible, so it's used for tool handles. It also takes finishes (see next page) well.

4) Beech is pinkish-brown. It's hard enough to resist being dented, and can be bent using steam. It's used for chairs and toys.

Wood Must be Felled...

1) Trees, e.g. from a plantation or a forest, are felled (cut down).

2) If the tree is from a plantation or sustainably managed forest, other trees will be planted to replace it.

3) The bark is removed, and the trunk is sawn up. Which way it's sawn affects how the planks will look, and how much they're likely to bend or warp (twist).

4) The wood is then seasoned by drying it — this makes the wood stronger and less likely to rot or twist.

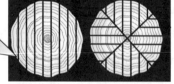
Slab sawn   Quarter sawn

Dozens of tiny trees are eating me — aaargh, Parana Pine...

Wood you be able to remember these facts if I teak away the page and ash you a question? I bet knot.
Don't pine away though — just take some time to try and learn them. Then life'll be a beech.

Timber

...Cut Into a Useful Form...

Wood can be bought in lots of <u>forms</u>:

1) Wood comes in different <u>sizes</u> — for example <u>planks</u> and <u>strips</u> are sold in standard lengths.

2) <u>Planed Square Edge</u> (<u>PSE</u>) wood has its rough surfaces shaved off with an electric <u>planer</u>.

3) <u>Rough sawn</u> wood is <u>not smoothed</u> after it's cut — so it's <u>cheaper</u> and useful for construction work where it <u>won't be visible</u>.

4) <u>Mouldings</u> are hardwood strips that come in a range of cross-sections. They're used for skirting boards, door frames and picture frames.

5) <u>Veneers</u> are thin cuts of wood that are glued onto other materials to give them a nicer appearance.

...And Finished to Protect It

Most woods need <u>protection</u>, particularly if they're going to be used <u>outdoors</u>.

1) You can apply <u>woodstain</u> to wood to enhance the appearance of its <u>grain</u>. It's available in natural colours but also in bright blues, reds, etc. Stains don't usually protect the wood, so you might need to apply varnish afterwards.

2) <u>Oil</u> can be used to maintain the wood's <u>natural</u> appearance. Some oil-based finishes also offer protection to wood used outdoors.

3) <u>Paint</u> is often used to colour and <u>protect</u> wood. <u>Emulsion paints</u> are cheap, but they are <u>water-based</u>, so they don't protect wood from water. <u>Polyurethane paint</u> is more expensive but is <u>waterproof</u> and much <u>tougher</u>.

4) <u>Polyurethane varnish</u> can be used to seal and protect the surface of the wood, and give it a smooth surface finish. You can buy it clear or in a wide range of colours.

Most hardwoods have an <u>attractive grain</u> — so you might want to use clear varnish rather than paint as a surface finish, e.g. oak furniture is often varnished.

Practice Questions

1) a) Give an example of a softwood.
   b) Describe its <u>appearance</u>.

2) a) Give an example of a hardwood that's often used for furniture.
   b) Describe its <u>appearance</u>.

3) Why are hardwoods generally more <u>expensive</u> than softwoods?

4) Why is wood <u>seasoned</u> after being felled?

5) Michael is making a wardrobe. He is using some <u>rough sawn wood</u> from a DIY store. What might he have to <u>do to the wood</u> first?

6) Wood can be <u>protected</u> by painting it.
   a) Suggest what type of wood was used to make this table.
   b) Why might the table have been coated in <u>clear varnish</u> rather than paint?

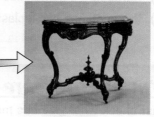

Section 4 — Materials and Components

Manufactured Boards

Boards are made by glueing together sheets, blocks, chips or fibres of wood.

There are Five Sorts of Board You Need to Know About

Plywood — Loads of Layers

1) Plywood is a very popular board, used for building and general construction.

2) Plywood is made up of layers of wood glued with their grain at 90 degrees to each other. This makes it very strong for its weight compared to wood.

3) It can be bent, which makes it useful for curved furniture.

4) The outside of the board can be finished with a nice veneer (a thin layer of good quality wood) to make it look better.

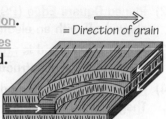
= Direction of grain

Blockboard — Blocks in a 'Sandwich'

1) Blockboard isn't as strong as plywood but it's a cheap substitute when you need thicker board.

2) Strips of softwood (usually pine or spruce) between 7 mm and 25 mm thick are glued together, side by side, and sandwiched between one or two layers of veneer on each side.

3) The veneers add strength and make the board look nicer.

4) The outer veneers are glued with their grain at right angles to the grain of the inner core — this makes the board stronger.

Veneers
Strips of softwood

Chipboard — Woodchips Squidged Together

1) Chipboard is cheap but not very strong.

2) It's produced by compressing wood particles together with glue.

3) It's usually used with a hardwood or plastic veneered surface.

4) It's used for table-tops and cheap furniture.

MDF — Fibres Squidged Together

1) Medium Density Fibreboard (MDF) is a popular board that's pretty cheap.

2) Softwood is broken down into tiny fibres, mixed with glue, heated and compressed into panels. It's denser and stronger than chipboard and doesn't warp if it gets damp.

3) MDF has smooth faces and takes paint and other finishes well. So it's often painted or has a veneer on top, and used for shelves and furniture.

Hardboard — Like a Thinner MDF

1) Hardboard is a cheap board. It's like MDF but thinner and more dense.

2) Tiny fibres are compressed together with glue into panels that have one smooth side and one textured side.

3) Hardboard's sometimes used as a cheap alternative to plywood.

4) It sometimes has a plastic surface on one side, and is used for cupboard backs and drawer bottoms.

I'm board — are we nearly there yet...

Just check what size bits make up the board — soon you'll be able to spot them at twenty paces...

Manufactured Boards

Boards Come in Stock Sizes

Boards come in a <u>range of sizes</u>. This means that manufacturers can buy the size that <u>best suits</u> what they're making and don't end up <u>wasting</u> loads of material.

Some 12 mm plywood   A 39 megaterabyte circuitboard

1) Boards are usually sold in sheets <u>2440 mm long</u> by <u>1220 mm wide</u> (8 by 4 feet in old money), or in <u>half sheets</u> (1220 x 1220 mm). You can also buy some <u>smaller</u> sizes.

2) They're available in a range of <u>thicknesses</u> that usually go up in 3 mm intervals (3 mm, 6 mm, 9 mm, etc.).

3) <u>Pegboard</u> is board with holes already punched in — ready for putting hooks in or attaching shelves.

4) <u>Mouldings</u> made of MDF come in set sizes and are used for things like <u>picture rails</u> and <u>door panels</u>.

A 2 bunny skateboard   A unifromage cheeseboard

Finishes Protect and Improve the Appearance of Boards

1) You can <u>paint</u> boards, but it's a good idea to <u>seal</u> them first (e.g. with watered-down PVA or MDF sealer) — otherwise the <u>cut edges</u> can soak up so much paint that they need <u>several coats</u>.

2) Boards with a <u>hardwood veneer</u> can be finished in the same way as <u>timber</u> (e.g. varnished, stained — see page 35).

3) You can apply a thin plastic layer called a <u>laminate</u>. These can be coloured (e.g. white covered chipboard) or have a wood grain picture underneath (e.g. wood-patterned plywood laminate flooring).

Practice Questions

1) <u>Blockboard</u> is a type of manufactured board.
   a) <u>Sketch</u> a diagram to show its construction.
   b) If you wanted a <u>stronger</u> board, what type could you use instead?
   c) What would be the <u>drawback</u> of using that type of board?

2) What <u>two processes</u> turn wood particles into boards like chipboard and MDF?

3) Give a use of:
   a) plywood,
   b) hardboard.

4) Jane wants to make an MDF table top that's 1800 mm wide and 2400 mm long.
   a) How many <u>standard-sized sheets</u> will she need to use?
   b) What might happen if she painted it <u>without sealing it</u> first?

5) Dave is making a cupboard using plywood. Suggest how he could <u>finish</u> it so that it looks like it was made using a <u>hardwood</u>.

Metals

There are hundreds of types and shapes of metal. Luckily, you only need to learn a few.

Different Metals Have Different Properties

1) Metals can be either ferrous (contain iron) or non-ferrous (contain no iron).
2) Metals can be mixed together to form alloys — for example, copper + zinc = brass. This means that you can get the best properties of each metal — brass is harder and stronger than pure copper or zinc.

Ferrous and non-ferrous metals	Properties	Uses
CAST IRON Grey.	Very strong if compressed, but brittle and may crack if dropped.	Bench vices, car brake discs, manhole covers
MILD STEEL (iron + carbon) Dull silver, or dark grey unless cleaned.	Quite strong and cheap, but rusts easily.	Car bodies, screws, nuts, bolts, nails.
STAINLESS STEEL (iron + carbon + chromium + nickel) Shiny and silvery.	Hard, won't rust, but more expensive than mild steel.	Surgical equipment, sinks, kettles, cutlery.
ALUMINIUM Light grey colour.	Lightweight, resistant to corrosion, expensive, not as strong as steel.	Aeroplane bodies, cans, ladders.
ZINC Bluish grey.	Not very strong, resists corrosion.	Coating steel (e.g. on nails, watering cans and buckets).
COPPER Reddish gold.	Fairly soft, malleable, ductile, very good electrical conductor.	Wiring, pipes, pans.
BRASS (copper + zinc) Yellowy.	Strong, resists corrosion, malleable, ductile, electrical conductor.	Door handles, taps, locks, electrical parts.
SILVER Silvery white.	Soft, malleable, ductile, very good electrical conductor, expensive.	Jewellery, expensive cutlery.
PEWTER (tin + copper + antimony) Silvery blue.	Soft, cheaper than silver.	Jewellery, small ornaments.

Metals Come in a Range of Shapes and Sizes

1) Metals are commonly available in a wide range of shapes and sizes.
2) This means that the manufacturers can buy roughly the right shape to start working with. For example...

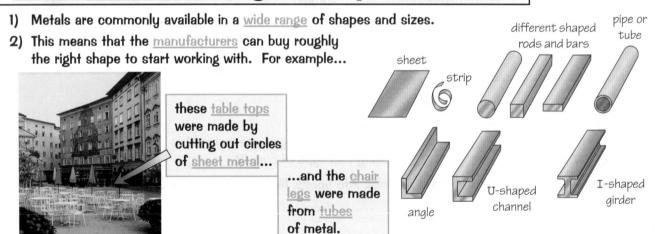

these table tops were made by cutting out circles of sheet metal...

...and the chair legs were made from tubes of metal.

Different sorts of metal — glam, heavy, thrash, nu...

Don't think that you'll never learn all the metals on this page. Just get a picture in your head of something made of each one (a metal image... ahaha), and its properties will be easier to remember.

Section 4 — Materials and Components

Metals

Metals are Extracted, Crushed, Refined, Cast and Rolled

1) Metal is extracted from the earth in the form of metal ore.
2) The ore is crushed and heated in a blast furnace until it melts.
3) It's then refined to get rid of impurities (unwanted materials).
4) The molten metal is cast (poured into a mould and cooled).
5) The metal can then be run through rollers to shape it.

Heat Treatments Soften or Toughen Metals

Metals can be heat-treated to change their properties. There are three main types of treatment:

1) Annealing — heating the metal and leaving it to cool slowly.
This makes it softer, more ductile and less brittle.

2) Hardening — heating and rapidly cooling a metal. This makes it, erm... harder.
The metal is heated till it's red hot then plunged into cold water or oil.
This leaves the metal brittle, so hardening is often followed by tempering...

3) Tempering — to make the metal tougher and less likely to break.
When steel is tempered, it's first cleaned (to make it bright in appearance) and then gently heated. As it gets hotter, it gradually changes colour — and the colour shows how tough it's become.

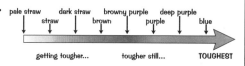

pale straw   dark straw   browny purple   deep purple
       straw   brown   purple   blue
getting tougher...   tougher still...   TOUGHEST

Metal Can be Coated for Protection

1) **PAINTING** A primer such as red oxide or zinc chromate is needed for steel (so that later coats of paint can form a strong bond to the surface). After the primer you need a top coat. A range of colours and finishes are available, and some give a very durable, weatherproof finish for outdoor use.

2) **PLASTIC COATING** A metal is heated evenly in an oven and then plunged into fluidised powder (very fine powder that's made to act like a liquid by passing gas through it) for a few seconds. The metal, with this thin coating of plastic, is then put back in the oven and the plastic fuses to the surface.

3) **PLATING** A metal object can be coated with a thin layer of a corrosion-resistant metal by electrolysis. The object is put in a bath of chemicals including the dissolved corrosion-resistant metal. An electric current is used to make the corrosion resistant metal solidify onto the object.

4) **LACQUERING** A thin layer of cellulose, gum or varnish is applied to leave a transparent coating. This provides a barrier against tarnishing and oxidising, and is often used on decorative items such as jewellery.

Tarnishing and oxidising make metal look dull.

Practice Questions

1) a) What is a ferrous metal?
   b) Name two non-ferrous metals.

2) a) Explain why steel is an alloy.
   b) Name an alloy other than steel.
   c) Explain why stainless steel is useful for making products that are used outdoors.

3) a) Name the process that's used to plate metals.
   b) What sort of metal would you plate mild steel with? Give an example of this type of metal.

40

Plastics

Next up, plastics. There are <u>two main sorts</u>:

1) <u>Thermoplastics</u> — ones that are <u>moulded</u> by heating and, if heated again, <u>can be remoulded</u>.
2) <u>Thermosetting</u> — once they've been moulded, they <u>cannot be remoulded</u>.

Thermoplastics — Recyclable **and Bendy**

EXAM TIP
You need to be able to <u>identify</u> these different plastics.

1) **Thermoplastics** are <u>easily formed</u> into shapes, but <u>don't resist heat</u> well.
2) **This means they're <u>easy to recycle</u> — they're <u>ground down</u>, <u>melted</u> and <u>re-used</u>.**

Thermoplastic	Properties and Uses
Acetate	Hard, transparent (see-through) and flexible. Used for overhead projector transparencies and packaging.
Acrylic	Hard and shiny. Resists weather well. Can be used to make motorcycle helmet visors, baths, signs, etc.
Low-density polyethylene (LDPE)	Soft and flexible. Used for packaging, carrier bags, washing-up liquid bottles, and to laminate paper (see p. 33).
High-density polyethylene (HDPE)	Stiff and strong but lightweight. Used for things like washing-up bowls, baskets, folding chairs and gas and water pipes.
Polyesters e.g. polyethylene terephthalate (PET)	PET is light, strong and tough. Used to make see-through drink bottles and fibres for clothes (see p. 45).
Expanded polystyrene (PS) e.g. STYROFOAM™	White, lightweight, crumbly. Used in packaging to protect and insulate. Easily shaped with a hot-wire cutter to make 3D mock-ups and models.
High impact polystyrene (HIPS)	Rigid and fairly cheap. Used for vacuum forming and fabricating boxes like CD cases or smoke detector casings.
Polyvinyl chloride (PVC)	Quite brittle, cheap and durable. Used for blister packs, window frames, vinyl records and some clothing.

Thermosetting **Plastics are** Non-Recyclable **and Rigid**

1) **Thermosetting plastics <u>resist heat</u> and <u>fire</u> (so they're used for electrical fittings and pan handles).**
2) **They undergo a <u>chemical change</u> when heated (unlike thermoplastics) to become <u>hard and rigid</u>.**
3) **This means they're <u>non-recyclable</u>.**

Thermosetting Plastic	Properties and Uses
Epoxy Resin (ER)	Rigid, durable and corrosion resistant. Used for circuit boards and wind turbine rotor blades.
Urea Formaldehyde (UF)	Hard, brittle and a good electrical insulator. Used for things like plug sockets and cupboard handles.
Melamine Formaldehyde (MF)	Strong and scratch-proof. Used to laminate chipboard (see p. 36) and for plates and bowls.
Glass Reinforced Plastic (GRP)	A thermosetting plastic mixed with glass strands to make it really strong. Used for racing car bodies and light aeroplanes.

Recycling — it's not biking back the way you came...

Thermosetting plastics can't be remoulded — once they're set, they're set permanently. Like when you pull a funny face and the wind changes. Something like that, anyway...

Section 4 — Materials and Components

Plastics

Plastics are Mostly Made From Oil

Plastics are mostly <u>synthetic</u> (made from crude <u>oil</u>, and sometimes gas and coal) — but a few are <u>natural</u> (made from <u>plants</u>).

1) Oil is <u>extracted</u> from underground by <u>drilling</u>.

2) It's heated in a <u>refinery</u> which <u>separates</u> it into different chemicals. This is called <u>fractional distillation</u>.

3) Some of the chemicals can be linked together to make <u>plastics</u>:

- • The chemicals that get joined together are called <u>monomers</u>.
- • The joined up monomers are known as <u>polymers</u>.
- • So the <u>process</u> is called <u>polymerisation</u>.

Monomers

Polymer

Polymerisation

4) Different chemicals can be added to the polymer to change the plastic's <u>properties</u>:

- • <u>Plasticisers</u> help the plastic <u>flow</u> better when it's melted, and make it <u>less brittle</u>.
- • <u>Fillers</u> (things like limestone or sawdust) can make plastic <u>stronger</u>, <u>harder</u> or more <u>rigid</u>.
- • <u>Blowing agents</u> turn plastic into <u>foam</u> (e.g. expanded PS), making it <u>lighter</u> and a <u>better insulator</u>.

5) Plastics come in a range of <u>shapes and sizes</u>:

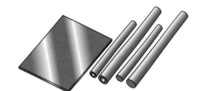

<u>Films</u> and <u>rolls</u> are good for <u>vacuum forming</u> (p. 74), and for packaging with <u>windows</u> (so the product is visible).

<u>Foam</u> is used for <u>protective packaging</u> and making <u>models</u> and <u>mock-ups</u>.

<u>Sheets</u>, <u>rods</u> and <u>tubes</u> can be cut to size and bent (see p. 73).

<u>Granules</u> are used by manufacturers — they're <u>melted down</u> and used in <u>injection moulding</u> and <u>extrusion</u> (see p. 75).

Plastics Don't Need Surface Finishes

1) Plastics don't need protective surface finishes because they're very <u>resistant</u> to <u>corrosion</u> and <u>decay</u>.

2) But for a nice appearance, you can use <u>wet and dry paper</u> (silicon carbide paper) to remove scratches from the plastic, and follow that up with a mild abrasive polish or anti-static cream.

3) Or, you could use a <u>buffing machine</u>.

Practice Questions

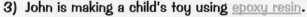

1) a) Why are thermosetting plastics <u>non-recyclable</u>?
   b) Give an example of a thermoplastic.

2) Rachel is designing a <u>saucepan</u>. Suggest a suitable plastic she could use to make the knob on the lid. Explain your answer.

3) John is making a child's toy using <u>epoxy resin</u>.
   a) Explain why epoxy resin doesn't need a protective surface finish.
   b) How could John remove any scratches from the surface of the epoxy resin?

4) Outline how most plastics are <u>made</u>.

Ceramics

Ceramics include clays, and also some other hard non-metals that you need to know about.

Ceramic Products are Often Made Using Clay

1) One of the main materials used to make ceramics is <u>clay</u>, which is dug from the <u>ground</u>.
2) Clays are <u>malleable</u> when moist and can be <u>hardened</u> by heating them to high temperatures (<u>firing</u>).
3) Moist, unhardened clay is called '<u>body clay</u>'. It's sold <u>by weight</u>.
4) Clay's <u>properties</u> can be altered by changing its <u>composition</u>, e.g. adding <u>bentonite</u> to make it more <u>malleable</u>, <u>flint</u> to make it <u>shrink less</u> when it's <u>fired</u>, or <u>grog</u> (small bits of previously fired clay) to make it less likely to <u>crack when it's fired</u>.

Different Types of Clay

EARTHENWARE CLAYS
<u>Cheap</u> and <u>easily available</u>. Often a <u>red-brown</u> colour. <u>Permeable</u> when fired but can be made watertight by <u>glazing</u>. Used for tiles, sewer pipes, pots and some tableware.

STONEWARE CLAYS
<u>Better quality</u> clay, often used for tableware. <u>Whitish</u> in colour. <u>Often glazed</u> (see below) to improve its looks.

CHINA CLAY
<u>Bright white</u>, and <u>harder</u> than earthenware and stoneware (it <u>won't scratch easily</u>). Used to make <u>porcelain</u>, for quality tableware and ornaments.

ST. THOMAS' CLAY
Often contains lots of <u>grog</u>. Used for <u>hand-built</u> sculptures. Can be thrown on a potter's wheel to make <u>pots</u>.

5) To make ceramics, body clay is moulded into shape by <u>hand</u> or on a <u>potter's wheel</u>. Alternatively, liquid clay can be poured into <u>moulds</u>. Then it's <u>dried slowly</u> to avoid cracking and distortion.
6) Watered down clay (called '<u>slip</u>') is used to help stick bits of clay together.
7) When dry, the clay is <u>fired</u> by heating it to about 1100 °C in a <u>kiln</u> (oven). This <u>fuses</u> the clay together and <u>removes</u> all the <u>moisture</u>. <u>Higher</u> firing <u>temperatures</u> make ceramics <u>more dense</u> (meaning they're <u>stronger</u>) and <u>less porous</u> (meaning the <u>glaze</u> doesn't <u>stick</u> as easily).

Ceramics Can be Finished With a Glaze

A glaze is a thin, shiny outer coating. The glaze is applied and the ceramic is <u>re-fired</u>. It then hardens to <u>seal the surface</u> and give the ceramic an <u>attractive finish</u>.

Glazes can be <u>transparent</u> or <u>coloured</u> with <u>pigments</u> such as <u>iron oxide</u> or <u>cobalt carbonate</u>. The <u>exact colour</u> that's produced depends on the <u>mixture of chemicals</u> and <u>how they're fired</u>.

<u>Underglazes</u> (e.g. a decorative pattern) can be applied to the surface of the pottery <u>before glazing</u>. Then, a transparent glaze can be applied <u>over the decoration</u>.

You can get different patterns and effects by firing in <u>different temperatures and conditions</u>:
- <u>Raku</u> — the ceramic is <u>removed</u> from the kiln while it's <u>still hot</u>, for <u>cracked glaze effects</u>.
- <u>Pit firing</u> — fired in a hole in the ground. The ceramic can be sprinkled with dry pigments to give <u>interesting markings</u>.
- <u>Saggar</u> — firing inside <u>boxes</u> that are filled with <u>combustible materials</u>, making random <u>scorched patterns</u>.

Ceramics making you potty — try not to glaze over...

Clays and glazes both come in a range of <u>mixtures</u> that can be <u>tweaked</u> to make the ceramic just right. Sort of like cooking with mud and glass, only less messy, and more likely to make a useful product.

Ceramics

Not All Ceramics are Made From Clay

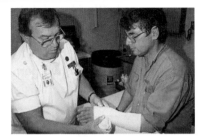

PLASTER OF PARIS — White and easily scratched. Made from a powder that's mixed with water and left to set. Can be used for artistic sculptures, and to make casts for broken bones.

CONCRETE — Grey and hard. Used for building foundations, and also floors and walls. Made from a mix of cement, water, sand and aggregate (crushed rocks), which is left to set.

GLASS — Smooth, hard and transparent. Used for bottles and windows. Made by melting sand with other minerals.

Ceramics Aren't Just Used for Pottery

1) Ceramics can resist high temperatures without melting. This means they can be used in spark plugs, light bulbs and heat-shield tiles on space shuttles.

2) They're good electrical insulators (don't let electrical current pass through), so they're used to separate electrical power lines from the pylons.

"Next knight to joust — Sir Amicks"

3) Ceramics can be used to make kitchen knives — they stay sharp and don't rust but are very expensive to manufacture.

4) New ceramic materials are being developed with useful properties:
   - Beryllium oxide-based ceramics have really high melting temperatures — so high that they can be used inside nuclear reactors.
   - Aluminium oxide and boron carbide based ceramics are really hard — so they're used in body and tank armour.

Practice Questions

1) a) Name two types of clay.
   b) How is clay obtained?

2) How can the properties of a clay be improved?

3) Harry the potter wants to make some roofing tiles. Which type of clay would be best for this?

4) What is 'slip'? What is it used for?

5) Peter is adding a glaze to his ceramic bowl. Suggest why he is doing this.

6) Give two examples of the use of ceramics in the electrical industry. For each example, say what properties of ceramics make them useful for that purpose.

Textiles

Fibres Are Spun Into the Yarns Used to Make Fabrics

1) Fibres are tiny 'hairs' that are spun into yarns — the threads that are woven or knitted into fabrics.

2) Fibres come in either short lengths (staple fibres), or longer lengths (filaments).
Filaments can be cut up into staple lengths if required.

3) Yarns are available in different thicknesses. A 1-ply yarn is a single yarn, a 2-ply yarn is two yarns twisted together, a 3-ply yarn is three yarns twisted together... and so on...

Yarns made from filaments are smooth...

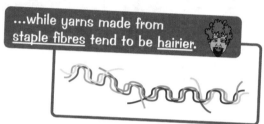

...while yarns made from staple fibres tend to be hairier.

Natural Fibres Are Harvested and Processed

1) Natural fibres are fibres obtained from natural sources (plants and animals).
They are harvested and processed before being spun into yarn.

2) These fibres come from renewable sources (you can always produce more of them), so they're fairly sustainable. They're also biodegradable, and often recyclable.

3) In general, natural fibres are absorbent and strong when dry, but have poor resistance to biological damage, e.g. from moths and mould.

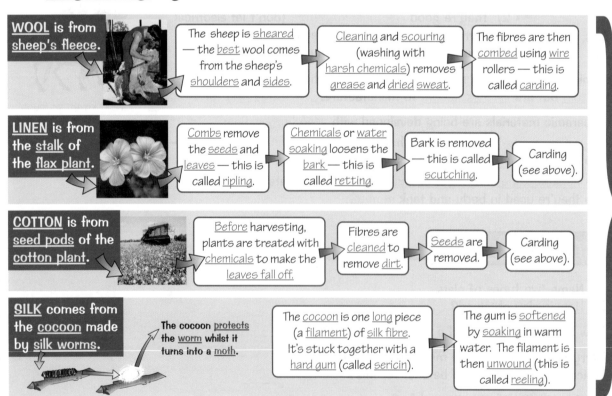

WOOL is from sheep's fleece.

The sheep is sheared — the best wool comes from the sheep's shoulders and sides.

Cleaning and scouring (washing with harsh chemicals) removes grease and dried sweat.

The fibres are then combed using wire rollers — this is called carding.

LINEN is from the stalk of the flax plant.

Combs remove the seeds and leaves — this is called ripling.

Chemicals or water soaking loosens the bark — this is called retting.

Bark is removed — this is called scutching.

Carding (see above).

COTTON is from seed pods of the cotton plant.

Before harvesting, plants are treated with chemicals to make the leaves fall off.

Fibres are cleaned to remove dirt.

Seeds are removed.

Carding (see above).

SILK comes from the cocoon made by silk worms.

The cocoon protects the worm whilst it turns into a moth.

The cocoon is one long piece (a filament) of silk fibre. It's stuck together with a hard gum (called sericin).

The gum is softened by soaking in warm water. The filament is then unwound (this is called reeling).

Fibres are now ready for spinning

After spinning into yarns, natural fibres need bleaching to give a uniform colour for dyeing. Both these processes involve the use of chemicals — so appropriate safety precautions are needed (see p. 62).

Don't yarn — textiles isn't that boring...

Make sure you can explain how each fibre is prepared — it's vital stuff and worth a few marks to boot...

Textiles

Synthetic Fibres Are Manufactured

1) Synthetic fibres are man-made fibres. They include polyester, polyamide (nylon), acrylic, elastane (LYCRA®) and TACTEL® (a microfibre made from nylon).
2) Synthetic fibres are less absorbent than natural fibres — so this means dying is harder.
3) They're made from polymers — long chains of monomers that come mainly from coal or oil. Because they're made from non-renewable resources, they're not sustainable fibres.

Polyester, LYCRA® and acrylic are produced from crude oil...

 Crude oil is a mixture of lots of different chemicals. To separate the chemicals you heat it. This is called fractional distillation.

Some of these chemicals (monomers) are made into polymers (polymerised). Different polymers will create different synthetic fibres.

The fibres are made by melting the polymer to form a liquid and forcing it through tiny holes. It's then cooled to form long filaments.

...and nylon is produced from coal.

 Coal is carbonised — it's heated in a container to make a sludge called coal tar.

Coal tar contains chemicals which are made into monomers. These are polymerised to form nylon filaments.

These filaments are then made into yarn.

The yarns are either wound onto spools, or chopped into staple lengths to be spun.

Fibres Are Woven, Knitted or Bonded to Make Fabrics

WOVEN FABRICS are made by interlacing two sets of yarns. Generally, woven fabrics don't stretch, are strong, flat and smooth, and are good for printing onto.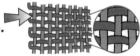
They're used for shirts, upholstery and trousers etc.

KNITTED FABRICS are made by interlocking one or more yarns together using loops. The loops trap air, so they insulate. They stretch more than woven fabrics.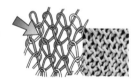
They're used for jumpers, socks, tights and swimwear etc.

BONDED FABRICS are non-woven 'webs' made of synthetic fibres (not yarns) glued or melted together. They don't fray  (when cut), but they're not stretchy and not very strong.
They're used for interfacing (putting in between layers of fabric for thickness, e.g. in collars).

> 1) Fabric comes on rolls of standard width, so you only need to specify the length you require.
> 2) Fabrics also come in different weights. The weight of a fabric depends on how tightly the fabric is knitted or woven, and on the thickness of the yarn used (i.e. 1 ply, 2 ply etc.).

Practice Questions

1) What are yarns?
2) Why are natural fibres more sustainable than synthetic fibres?
3) Name two synthetic fibres.
4) a) Give one advantage of bonded fabrics.
   b) Now give one disadvantage.
5) Which is the tastiest source of fibre — bran or prunes?

Textiles

Different Fibres *Give* Fabrics *With* Different Properties

	Fibre	Properties	Uses
Natural fibres	WOOL	<u>Good</u>: warm, absorbent, stretchy, crease resistant, low flammability <u>Bad</u>: can shrink when washed, dries slowly, can feel itchy.	Woven in suits. Knitted in jumpers and dresses.
	LINEN	<u>Good</u>: strong, hard-wearing, absorbent, comfortable, feels cool in hot weather. <u>Bad</u>: creases, high flammability, bad drape, expensive.	Woven in trousers and summer suits.
	COTTON	<u>Good</u>: strong, hard-wearing, absorbent, comfortable, feels cool in hot weather, cheap. <u>Bad</u>: creases, high flammability, can shrink, dries slowly.	Woven in jeans. Knitted in T-shirts, socks.
	SILK	<u>Good</u>: strong, smooth, absorbent, good drape, low flammability, comfortable. <u>Bad</u>: creases, doesn't wash well, weak when wet, expensive.	Woven in lingerie, ties and shirts.
Synthetic fibres	POLYESTER	<u>Good</u>: strong, hard wearing, low flammability, cheap, resists creasing, dries quickly, good elasticity. <u>Bad</u>: not absorbent.	Knitted in sportswear. Woven in bedsheets.
	NYLON	<u>Good</u>: strong, hard wearing, warm, fairly cheap, good elasticity. <u>Bad</u>: not absorbent, damaged by sunlight, melts as it burns.	Knitted in sportswear, and clothing.
	ACRYLIC	<u>Good</u>: strong, warm, good elasticity, crease resistant, lightweight, doesn't shrink, cheap. <u>Bad</u>: not very absorbent, high flammability.	Knitted in jumpers. Also used in fake fur.
	ELASTANE	<u>Good</u>: extremely elastic, strong, hard wearing, lightweight. <u>Bad</u>: not absorbent, high flammability.	Mixed (see below) with other yarns to give stretch.
	TACTEL® (microfibre)	(These are really, really thin fibres) <u>Good</u>: very lightweight, strong, water repellent, breathable, good feel. <u>Bad</u>: expensive.	Knitted in sportswear. Woven in water-repellent outdoor wear.

Fibres *Can Be Combined by* Blending *or* Mixing

Fabrics made from a <u>combination</u> of different <u>fibres</u> can give you <u>better</u> properties.

There are <u>two ways</u> of combining fibres to get fabrics with combined properties — <u>blending</u> fibres within yarns, and <u>mixing</u> different yarns (where each yarn is made from one type of fibre). Here's how:

1) A **BLEND** is when two or more <u>different fibres</u> are combined to produce a <u>yarn</u>.

2) This mixed yarn is then <u>woven</u> or <u>knitted</u> to make a fabric.

EXAMPLE

Combining <u>cotton</u> and <u>polyester</u> fibres is one of the most common <u>blended</u> fabrics. The resulting fabric:
- is even <u>stronger</u> and remains <u>hard-wearing</u>
- is <u>less absorbent</u> — so dries more quickly
- is <u>soft</u> and <u>comfortable</u>
- resists <u>creasing</u> (is easier to iron)
- <u>doesn't shrink</u> easily
- BUT is <u>highly flammable</u>

1) A **MIX** is when a fabric is made up of two or more <u>different types of yarn</u>.

2) The <u>two</u> different types of yarn can then be <u>knitted</u> or <u>woven</u> together to make a fabric.

EXAMPLE

<u>Elastane</u> (LYCRA®) is commonly <u>mixed</u> with <u>cotton</u>. The resulting fabric:
- remains <u>strong</u>
- <u>stretches</u> to fit snugly
- is <u>comfortable</u> to <u>move</u> in
- <u>resists creasing</u>
- can be <u>dyed</u> easily

Mixed fibres — not like putting prunes on your bran flakes...

Mixing and blending fibres is really useful — you get a whole load of new <u>properties</u> to play with...

Textiles

Finishes Improve The Performance of Fabrics

Chemicals are applied to fibres or fabrics during manufacturing to give fabrics beneficial properties.

FLAME RETARDANCE

1) Flame retardant finishes are chemicals that make fabrics less likely to catch fire.

2) They're often used on flammable fibres like cotton. Products they're used on include racing drivers' and welders' overalls, night clothes and fabric for soft furnishings.

Using a fire retardant finish on fabrics like cotton makes the fabric slightly stiffer.

WATER RESISTANCE

1) Chemicals (e.g. silicones) can be applied to the surface of fabrics to stop water droplets passing through.

The water forms beads on the surface.

2) Nylon is often given a water resistant finish and used to make coats and tents.

These finishes don't make the fabric waterproof — if the surface becomes saturated (completely covered in water) the water will leak through.

STAIN RESISTANCE

1) Fabrics can be made stain resistant with a finish of a mixture of silicone and fluorine or a teflon coating (also used on non-stick frying pans).

2) These finishes stop grease and dirt from penetrating the fabric.

3) Stain resistant finishes are used a lot on carpets and upholstery.

CREASE RESISTANCE

1) These finishes are given to fabrics that crease easily (e.g. cotton and linen).

2) However, the chemicals or resins used can make fabrics feel slightly stiffer.

SHRINK RESISTANCE

1) These finishes are applied to fabrics such as wool, which may shrink when machine washed.

2) Scales on wool fibres cause wool to shrink in the wash. Hot water and rubbing cause the fibres to move against each other and the scales tangle and lock together.

3) To stop this, the scales can be permanently removed with chlorine, or a coating applied to smooth the surface of the fibres.

Practice Questions

1) Sam is making a summer suit from linen.
   a) Give two advantages of using linen for a summer suit.
   b) Give two disadvantages of using linen.

2) Peter wants to use a really stretchy fabric for his fancy dress costume. Suggest a fabric he could use.

3) a) Why are some fabrics made by combining fibres?
   b) Give two ways of combining fibres.
   c) What is the difference between these two methods?

4) Give three different finishes that can be added to fabrics to improve their properties.

5) Suggest a fabric and finish that would be suitable for this fireman's jacket?

Food

Finally, a design material you can eat. Yes, it's time for food materials — or <u>ingredients</u> to you and me.

Food Materials Provide Different Nutrients...

SUGARS
1) <u>Sugars</u> are a source of <u>energy</u>.
2) You can get <u>pure sugar</u> (e.g. <u>granulated</u>, <u>brown</u> and <u>icing sugar</u>) but it's also found in <u>honey</u> and <u>fruit</u>.

Sugar, starch and fibre are all types of carbohydrates.

STARCH
1) <u>Starch</u> is a complex sugar that must be <u>broken down</u> by <u>digestion</u> before its energy can be used.
2) Starch is found in <u>potatoes</u> and <u>flour</u> (and things made with flour, e.g. bread and pasta).

FIBRE
1) <u>Fibre cannot</u> be <u>digested</u> and doesn't have any nutritional value. However, it's <u>important</u> for the <u>healthy</u> functioning of the <u>digestive system</u>.
2) It's found in <u>fruit</u>, <u>vegetables</u>, <u>bran</u>, <u>beans</u> and <u>pasta</u>.

PROTEIN
1) <u>Protein</u> is needed by our bodies to <u>build</u> and <u>repair muscles</u>, <u>tissues</u> and <u>organs</u>.
2) Protein is found in <u>meat</u>, <u>fish</u>, <u>milk</u>, <u>beans</u> and <u>eggs</u> as well as meat <u>replacement</u> products (e.g. <u>tofu</u>).

FATS
1) <u>Fats</u> are a concentrated energy source. You need a certain amount of body fat to stay <u>warm</u>.
2) They include <u>butter</u>, <u>margarine</u>, <u>lard</u>, <u>suet</u> and <u>oils</u> (e.g. olive or sunflower oil).

<u>VITAMINS</u> and <u>MINERALS</u> are <u>essential</u> — they help other nutrients work and can prevent <u>diseases</u>.

1) <u>VITAMIN A</u> is made from retinol, which is found in <u>liver</u>, <u>butter</u>, <u>oily fish</u> and <u>eggs</u>. We can also make it from carotene, which is mostly found in <u>orange</u> or <u>yellow fruit</u> and <u>veg</u>. It's needed for good eyesight (especially night vision) and the growth and function of tissues.

2) <u>VITAMIN B</u> is found in <u>cereals</u>, <u>peas</u>, <u>pulses</u>, <u>dairy produce</u>, <u>meat</u> and <u>fish</u>. B vitamins help with <u>growth</u>, the release of <u>energy</u> and the <u>repair</u> of tissues.

3) <u>VITAMIN C</u> is also known as ascorbic acid. It's found in <u>citrus fruits</u> (oranges and lemons), <u>green vegetables</u>, <u>peppers</u> and <u>potatoes</u>. It helps the body <u>absorb calcium</u> and <u>iron</u> from food, and keeps <u>blood vessels</u> healthy and heals <u>wounds</u>.

4) <u>VITAMIN D</u> is also known as calciferol. It's found in <u>oily fish</u> and <u>eggs</u>. It helps the body absorb calcium, and a lack of it can lead to bone diseases like rickets and osteoporosis.

5) <u>CALCIUM</u> is found in <u>milk</u>, <u>green leafy vegetables</u> and <u>white bread</u>. It's needed for strong <u>bones</u> and <u>teeth</u> and healthy <u>nerves</u> and <u>muscles</u>. Lack of calcium can lead to osteoporosis.

6) <u>IRON</u> is found in <u>dark green vegetables</u> (e.g. <u>spinach</u>) and <u>meat</u>. It's needed to form part of <u>haemoglobin</u> which allows <u>red blood cells</u> to carry <u>oxygen</u> around the body.

Lard... suet... butter — mmmm...

Finished this page — go and grab a snack, then come back for a second helping of food materials.

Food

...And Have Useful Working Characteristics

Some food materials have properties that are useful in the production of food products.

Butter

Adds flavour to foods like shortbread.

Rubbed into flour to make pastry and biscuits 'short' (crumbly).

Adds colour to pastry.

Fats

Enrich sauces — makes them thicker and taste better.

Sugar

...is a preservative in jam...

...is used to sweeten foods...

...and when heated it caramelises (forms a sweet tasting, brown liquid). It's used to top off desserts.

Flour

Added as a thickening agent, e.g. in sauces.

Glazing, e.g. brushing egg on bagels — for a glossy finish when cooked.

Coating or enrobing — eggs help dry ingredients like breadcrumbs to stick to food, e.g. chicken.

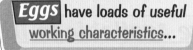

Eggs have loads of useful working characteristics...

Emulsification, e.g. in salad dressings. Lecithin found in eggs stops oil and water mixtures separating.

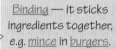

Binding — it sticks ingredients together, e.g. mince in burgers.

Thickening, e.g. in quiche. Eggs coagulate (turn solid) when heated.

Aeration, e.g. in cakes — when it's beaten, egg white traps air.

Practice Questions

1) Name two foods that contain starch.

2) Why do our bodies need protein?

3) a) What is vitamin C also known as?
   b) Which foods is it found in?

4) a) Give two working characteristics of sugar.
   b) Give two working characteristics of butter.
   c) Karen is making some chicken nuggets.
      What could she use to help stick the breadcrumbs to the chicken?

Food

Mmm, even more food materials to chew on — lucky you, get stuck in and gobble up these facts...

Food Materials Are Processed From Basic Food Sources

Basic food materials are first harvested and then processed before being sold to the consumer.

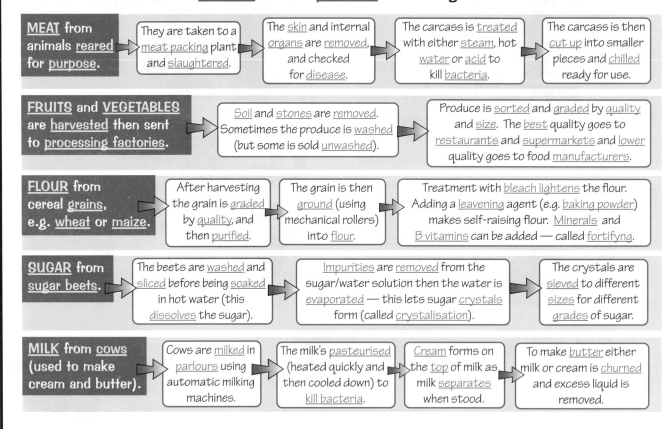

MEAT from animals reared for purpose. → They are taken to a meat packing plant and slaughtered. → The skin and internal organs are removed, and checked for disease. → The carcass is treated with either steam, hot water or acid to kill bacteria. → The carcass is then cut up into smaller pieces and chilled ready for use.

FRUITS and **VEGETABLES** are harvested then sent to processing factories. → Soil and stones are removed. Sometimes the produce is washed (but some is sold unwashed). → Produce is sorted and graded by quality and size. The best quality goes to restaurants and supermarkets and lower quality goes to food manufacturers.

FLOUR from cereal grains, e.g. wheat or maize. → After harvesting the grain is graded by quality, and then purified. → The grain is then ground (using mechanical rollers) into flour. → Treatment with bleach lightens the flour. Adding a leavening agent (e.g. baking powder) makes self-raising flour. Minerals and B vitamins can be added — called fortifying.

SUGAR from sugar beets. → The beets are washed and sliced before being soaked in hot water (this dissolves the sugar). → Impurities are removed from the sugar/water solution then the water is evaporated — this lets sugar crystals form (called crystalisation). → The crystals are sieved to different sizes for different grades of sugar.

MILK from cows (used to make cream and butter). → Cows are milked in parlours using automatic milking machines. → The milk's pasteurised (heated quickly and then cooled down) to kill bacteria. → Cream forms on the top of milk as milk separates when stood. → To make butter either milk or cream is churned and excess liquid is removed.

Food Components Are Available in Different Forms

Food components (the things you use to cook with) are available in different forms to the consumer. Which form you buy depends on what you're making, and also how long you're going to keep the food material before you use it all.

1) **LIQUIDS** — e.g. pasta sauces and fruit juices.
2) **FRESH** — doesn't last long but tastes better, e.g. fruit.
3) **DEHYDRATED** — moisture is removed so produce lasts longer, e.g. dried apricots.
4) **CANNED** — lasts for months or years if unopened — the can prevents micro-organisms entering.
5) **FROZEN** — stored in a freezer (-18 °C) which stops bacteria and mould growing, so food lasts longer.

Food Components Are Bought by Weight and Volume

1) Some foods are sold by how much they weigh — e.g. in grams (g) or kilograms (kg). Fresh meat, vegetables and cheese are sold in this way. These measurements are also used to specify the amount of food components in recipes.

2) Some food components are sold and measured by volume. Volume can be measured in litres (l) or millilitres (ml). Or, you can use common kitchen utensils, e.g. a teaspoon or a cup.

Food material — used for making edible clothes...

You buy food by volume and weight — right, I'll have a loud turnip and I don't want to wait long...

Food

Combining Ingredients *Gives* New Characteristics

How a product turns out depends on the ingredients you use and how they react with each other.

1. A **SOLUTION** forms when solid ingredients completely dissolve in a liquid, e.g. sugar dissolves in water to make a solution. You can't tell the separate ingredients apart once they've formed a solution.

sugar + water → a solution

2. A **SUSPENSION** forms when solid ingredients are added to a liquid but don't dissolve, e.g. flour mixed with water forms a cloudy suspension.

3. A **GEL** is like a thick solution, in between a liquid and a solid. Only a small amount of solid ingredient is needed to set a lot of liquid, e.g. a small amount of gelatine can set a lot of water to form jelly.

Some cold desserts are gels, e.g. jellies, mousses, cheesecakes.

There's a natural gelling agent in some fruits called pectin. It's released from these fruits during cooking and it helps foods like jams to set.

4. An **EMULSION** is formed when oily and watery liquids are mixed together and the droplets of one spread out through the other — they usually separate unless you keep shaking or stirring them. Emulsions need an emulsifier to stop the oil separating from the liquid, e.g. egg yolks (see p. 49).

Processing **Food Materials** *Gives* New Characteristics

Food materials can be processed to give new characteristics in food products.

Whisking traps air, e.g. whisked eggs are used in meringues.

Slicing and grating can change the way foods cook.

Mincing (grinding) changes texture, e.g. minced beef.

Practice Questions

1) a) Where does flour come from?
   b) Where does sugar come from?

2) Why might you treat flour with bleach during processing?

3) Why is milk pasteurised?

4) What is a gel?

5) Karen is making a salad dressing — an emulsion.
   a) What is an emulsion?
   b) How could she stop it from separating?

Electrical Components

Loads of <u>products</u> have an electrical system inside to <u>make them function</u>, from cars to alarm clocks.
<u>Electrical systems</u> are made up of lots of <u>electrical components</u> arranged in an <u>electrical circuit</u>.

Electrical Systems Involve Circuits

1) All <u>electrical systems</u> need to have a <u>complete circuit</u> to make them <u>work</u>. Here's a simple circuit:

The circuit isn't <u>complete</u> yet — there's a <u>gap</u> at the switch. When you press the switch down you make a complete circuit. An electric current flows and the lamp comes on.

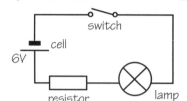

You can draw <u>diagrams</u> of electrical circuits using <u>symbols</u> to represent the components.

2) The materials you use in a circuit have to be <u>conductors</u> — they need to let electricity <u>flow through</u>. E.g. <u>copper</u> is used for the wire that joins the components because it's a <u>good conductor</u> and is <u>ductile</u>.

3) <u>Insulators</u> (e.g. PVC) don't let electricity through, so they're used to coat the outside of wires.

4) <u>Voltage</u> from a power cell (a battery) or the mains pushes the electric current around a circuit.

   - <u>Mains power</u> is used for <u>non-portable</u> products like fridges and televisions.
   - <u>Batteries</u> are used in <u>portable</u> products. There are <u>disposable</u> batteries and <u>rechargeable</u> ones.
   - <u>Rechargeable</u> batteries are more <u>expensive</u> than disposable batteries, but can be cheaper in the long run as you don't need to keep replacing them. They're <u>built in</u> to some products, e.g. mobile phones.

5) <u>Resistors</u> are used to <u>reduce</u> the current in a circuit so you don't damage delicate components (e.g. the lamp in the circuit above). Resistance is <u>measured</u> in <u>ohms</u> (Ω). A <u>larger</u> resistance means <u>less current</u> in the circuit.

Colour-coded <u>stripes</u> show the <u>resistance</u>.

6) <u>Transistors</u> are <u>electronic switches</u> — a small current is used to <u>switch on</u> a large current. E.g. in a heat sensor, a <u>small current</u> passing through a thermistor switches on a <u>larger current</u> to power a cooling fan.

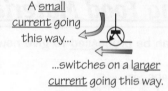

A <u>small current</u> going this way...

...switches on a <u>larger current</u> going this way.

7) <u>Capacitors store charge</u>. E.g. in a camera flash, a capacitor is <u>charged up</u> by the battery, allowing a <u>large</u> release of electrical current to <u>briefly</u> light a bright lamp. The amount of <u>charge stored</u> is rated in <u>farads</u> (F).

The capacitor <u>won't let</u> an electrical current pass across it.

When it's connected to a battery, one side gets positively <u>charged</u>, and the other side gets negatively <u>charged</u>.

A Circuit has an Input, a Process and an Output

1) A <u>system</u> can be broken down into three '<u>blocks</u>':

2) The <u>electric signal</u> passes from one block to the next.

3) Each block <u>changes</u> the signal in some way to allow the system to produce the required function.

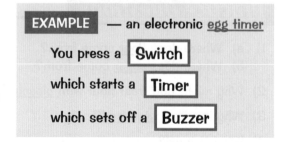

EXAMPLE — an electronic <u>egg timer</u>

You press a | Switch |

which starts a | Timer |

which sets off a | Buzzer |

Watch out for the cake — it's got an electric current...

Take some time to switch off and re-charge your batteries when revising. If your body's resisting relaxation, try this meditative chant — Ohm, Ohm, Ohhhmmm, Ohhhhmmmm. There, that's better...

Electrical Components

Input Devices Activate an Electrical Current

Input device	Symbol	Device	Function	Uses
Switches	open closed		Complete electrical circuits, allowing current to flow around them.	Light switches, 'on' switches.
Thermistor (temperature sensor)			Its resistance changes depending on temperature.	Thermostats in central heating.
Light-dependent resistor (senses light)			Its resistance changes depending on light levels.	Burglar detectors.

Output Devices Include Lamps, Motors, Buzzers...

Output device	Symbol	Device	Function	Uses
Lamp			Turns electrical energy into light.	Toys, security lights.
Speaker			Turns electrical signals into sound.	Telephones, headphones.
Motor			Converts electrical energy into rotational motion.	Powering mechanisms.
Solenoid			Converts electrical energy into small movements in a straight line, e.g. to open a valve or switch.	Locks, toys.
Buzzer			Converts electrical energy into noise.	Alarm clocks.

The input and output components can be arranged into circuits to produce different functions. For example, a circuit with a thermistor and a buzzer can act as a temperature sensor.

Integrated Circuits Combine Many Components

1) Integrated circuits (ICs) or 'chips' are tiny electrical circuits with many components built in.
2) They're used in loads of electronic products and replace discrete components.
3) They're built to perform particular functions e.g. storing data, keeping time.
4) Products like musical greetings cards use ICs that play a tune as you open the card. Calculators use ICs to do the mathematical operations.

Practice Questions

1) A simple system has three blocks. What are they?
2) a) What material is used to join the components in an electrical circuit?
   b) Explain why this is a suitable material.
3) Calum has designed an outdoor light that comes on when it gets dark. What type of input device might he have used in his circuit?
4) Juan is designing an alert buzzer that will go off when his greenhouse gets above a certain temperature. He decides to use a thermistor as an input device.
   a) What is a thermistor?
   b) What is the output device in this electrical system?

Mechanical Components

Mechanisms Change Input Motion into Output Motion

1) All mechanical systems have <u>mechanisms</u> which transform an <u>input motion</u> into an <u>output motion</u>.
2) They're <u>designed</u> so you can gain an <u>advantage</u> from using them — they make something easier to do.
3) Some mechanisms <u>change one type of motion into another</u>.

<u>Linear motion</u> is moving one way in a straight line. <u>Rotary motion</u> is moving in a circle.

Gear Trains Transmit or Change Rotary Motion

Gears are <u>toothed wheels</u> that <u>interlock</u>. A <u>gear train</u> is where two or more gears are <u>linked together</u>.

The <u>driver gear</u>, turned by hand or a motor, <u>turns the driven gear</u>. Both will automatically turn in <u>different directions</u>.

If you use a third gear (called an <u>idler</u>), the driver and the driven gears will both turn in the <u>same direction</u>. The size of the idler won't alter the speed of the other two gears.

If linked gears are different sizes, they will turn at <u>different speeds</u>. This driven gear has <u>half</u> as many teeth as the driver gear — so it'll turn <u>twice</u> in the time that the driver gear turns once.

Some gears can <u>change</u> the <u>type</u> or <u>direction</u> of motion...

RACK AND PINION GEARS
are used to <u>turn rotary</u> motion into <u>linear</u> motion.

The <u>pinion</u> is turned to move a flat gear, the <u>rack</u>. These are used on <u>railways</u> where the <u>track</u> is <u>steep</u> to stop the wheels <u>slipping</u> backwards.

A WORM DRIVE AND WORM WHEEL
change the direction of rotation through <u>90°</u>.

The worm <u>drive</u> (the driver) only has <u>one tooth</u> and will turn much <u>faster</u> than the worm <u>wheel</u>, which has many teeth so will turn very <u>slowly</u>. These are used for tightening <u>guitar</u> strings.

BEVEL GEARS
also <u>change the direction</u> of rotation through <u>90°</u>.

The teeth are angled at <u>45°</u> so the gears fit together at <u>right angles</u>.

Levers Are Used to Give a Mechanical Advantage

FIRST CLASS LEVERS have the <u>pivot</u> between the <u>effort</u> and the <u>load</u>. A <u>large load</u> can be lifted using a <u>smaller effort</u> (a <u>mechanical advantage</u>). As you move the <u>pivot closer to the load</u> it becomes <u>easier</u> to lift.

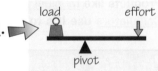

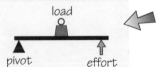

SECOND CLASS LEVERS have a <u>pivot</u> at one end of the lever and the <u>effort</u> is at the other end. The <u>closer</u> together the <u>pivot</u> and <u>load</u> are, the easier it is to lift.

In a **THIRD CLASS LEVER** the <u>effort</u> is between the <u>load</u> and the <u>pivot</u>. Moving the effort and pivot further <u>apart</u> makes it easier to move or lift the load.

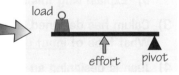

I always find inputting a spicy curry speeds up my motions...

Got your head geared up for mechanical systems yet? Good, because there's more on the next page...

Mechanical Components

Pulleys Help to Lift a Load

One pulley on its own changes the direction of the force required.
The same amount of force is needed but pulling down might be easier than lifting.

Using two or more pulleys together makes things feel lighter than they actually are.
One fixed pulley and one moving pulley (block and tackle) will mean you only need half the force to lift a load.

Linkages Connect Different Parts of a Mechanism

Simple linkages can transfer forces and change the direction of motion.

A bell crank changes the direction of a force through 90°.

Pneumatic Cylinders Use Compressed Air

Compressed air is used to push a piston down a cylinder — air pressure is converted into linear movement.

Single acting cylinders

Compressed air goes in here...
...and forces the piston out.
The spring moves the piston back.

Double acting cylinders

These have two air connections.
air connections

They work like single acting cylinders but the piston is pushed back with compressed air.

Chain and Sprocket Mechanisms Transfer Movement

1) These are found on bikes.
2) Two sprockets (toothed wheels) are linked with a chain (made up from loads of links).

As with gear trains, the size of the sprockets affects their speed.

Mechanical Components can be Combined in Systems

Cranes are systems that lift and move heavy loads.

1) They use pulleys to lift the load.
2) The top part of the crane rotates — this is done using bevel gears.
3) The arm of the crane is a third class lever. The load is balanced with concrete blocks.

Practice Questions

1) Peter is designing a product which uses a rack and pinion gear. What two types of motion does a rack and pinion involve?

2) Draw a sketch to show how a bell crank changes the direction of a force.

3) Nadia needs a mechanism that will help her to lift a heavy load of bricks.
   a) Suggest a mechanical system that could help with this.
   b) Explain how it helps.

4) Alistair is trying to lift a heavy load of turnips. He sets up the lever shown to the left.
   a) Suggest what he could change to make lifting the load easier.
   b) What type of lever is this — first, second or third class?

Fixings and Bindings

Ooh, I do like a good <u>fixing</u>. Even if you don't share my enthusiasm, you still have to know about them.

Fixings **Can Be** Permanent...

1) <u>Double-sided sticky pads</u> will stick things together <u>quickly</u>.

2) <u>Ratchet rivets</u> and <u>rapid-assembly post and screw</u> fixings will join sheets of <u>corrugated plastic</u> together.

3) <u>Snap rivets</u> are plastic clips used to <u>join sheet material</u> (e.g. plastic) together. They're installed from <u>one side</u> — first you make a <u>hole</u> through the sheets then push the top of the rivet by hand. See page 59 for more on rivets.

Push

...Or Temporary

<u>Velcro</u>® <u>pads</u> are self-adhesive pieces of a <u>two-part hook and loop system</u>. They've got loads of uses — they're particularly good for displays.

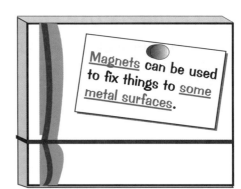

<u>Magnets</u> can be used to fix things to <u>some metal surfaces</u>.

<u>Press stud fastenings</u> are good for joining fabric bits together.

<u>Hooks</u> can be used to <u>hang</u> materials — they're useful when creating displays.

<u>Prong paper fasteners</u> join pieces of <u>paper</u> and <u>card</u> together as <u>movable joints</u>.

The fastener is inserted through a hole and then opened out.

<u>Treasury tags</u> hold paper together <u>loosely</u>. They're really cheap.

<u>Drawing pins</u> (also known as <u>thumb tacks</u> or <u>map pins</u>) are useful for fixing paper and card to <u>display boards</u>.

<u>Staples</u> are a <u>permanent</u> or <u>temporary fixing</u> for paper or thin card. You can <u>remove</u> them with a <u>staple-remover</u>.

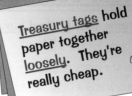

They know what staples are, Barney...

You're riveted by this page — I can see it's got you hooked...

Yes, yes, I know — you know most of this already. But, really, don't overlook the humble staple — think about all of the times it's saved your life. Probably just as many times as the little old paper clip.

Fixings and Bindings

Bindings hold <u>sheets of paper</u> together. There are lots of different types — which one you choose depends on <u>cost</u>, the <u>number</u> of sheets you need to hold and the <u>appearance</u> you want.

Some Bindings are Cheap and Cheerful...

1) In `comb binding` you <u>punch holes</u> in the sheets using a special <u>machine</u>, then put a <u>plastic comb</u> in. You can <u>add or remove</u> pages without causing damage and the bound book <u>opens flat</u>, making it <u>easy to read</u>.

2) In `spiral binding` a <u>plastic coil</u> is inserted down the spine. <u>Wiro binding</u> is similar to spiral but it uses a <u>double loop wire</u> instead of a plastic coil.

comb binding   spiral binding   wiro binding

3) `Saddle stitching` is where double sized pages are <u>folded</u> and <u>stapled</u> together at the centre. This type of binding is easy and cheap but it <u>won't hold many sheets</u>. Saddle stitched books open more or less <u>flat</u>. <u>This very book</u> you're reading now is saddle stitched.

...and Some are a Bit More Expensive

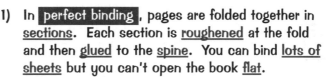

1) In `perfect binding`, pages are folded together in <u>sections</u>. Each section is <u>roughened</u> at the fold and then <u>glued</u> to the <u>spine</u>. You can bind <u>lots of sheets</u> but you can't open the book <u>flat</u>.

2) `Thread-sewing` is <u>expensive</u>. The pages are <u>sewn</u> together in sections, then a <u>soft cover</u> is <u>glued</u> on. The pages are less likely to come <u>loose</u> than with perfect binding.

3) `Case-Bound/Hard-Bound` books are like <u>thread-sewn</u> ones but with a <u>hard cover</u>.

> <u>Index tabs</u> help to sort a book into sections, making it <u>easier to find</u> parts because <u>flaps stick out</u>.

Practice Questions

1) Name three types of <u>permanent fixing</u>.

2) Tim is designing a <u>booklet</u> in which the pages will be fixed together at one corner.
   He then wants to attach the booklet to a <u>display board</u>.
   a) Name <u>two</u> types of <u>temporary fixing</u> that Tim could use
      to loosely hold together the sheets of paper in his booklet.
   b) How could Tim attach his booklet to a <u>display board</u>?

3) Dave needs to bind some copies of his design evaluation.
   He needs ten copies for his classmates and one copy for his teacher.
   a) Suggest how Dave could <u>cheaply</u> and <u>quickly</u> bind ten copies for his classmates.
   b) He binds his teacher's copy using <u>thread-sewing</u>. Give one <u>advantage</u> of thread sewing over perfect binding.

Standard Components

Standard components make life <u>easier</u> for designers and manufacturers.

Standard Components <u>Are</u> Pre-Manufactured <u>Parts</u>

1) Standard components are common fixings and parts that <u>manufacturers buy</u> instead of manufacturing them <u>themselves</u>, e.g. screws, rivets and buttons.

2) Standard components are <u>mass produced</u> so they're available at <u>low cost</u> to manufacturers.

3) Using standard components saves <u>time</u> during manufacture — it makes it more <u>efficient</u>.

4) <u>Specialist machinery</u> and <u>extra materials</u> aren't needed so it also saves <u>money</u>.

5) So, when <u>designers</u> are working on a new product, they need to think about which standard components they could use. When using CAD, designers can <u>select</u> standard components to use in their designs.

Different Products <u>Use Different</u> Standard Components

There are all sorts of standard components out there for use with different materials.

1) Manufacturers can buy <u>paper</u> in standard sizes and weights — see pages 32-33.

2) There are also plenty of <u>fixings</u> and <u>bindings</u> for use with paper and card — see pages 56-57.

3) <u>Mechanical components</u>, such as gears and pulleys (pages 54-55), can be bought in certain sizes.

4) Manufacturers can also buy standard components for <u>electrical circuits</u> (see pages 52-53).

 5) Then there are standard components for the <u>textile industry</u>. <u>Fastenings</u> (e.g. zips and buttons) can be bought ready-made and <u>threads</u> are available in a range of colours and thicknesses.

6) The same goes for the <u>food industry</u> — cake decorations and icing are often ready-made, along with pastry cases, pizza bases and things like stock cubes.

Screws <u>and Bolts</u> are Standard Components...

There are <u>different types</u> of screws for use with <u>wood</u>, <u>metals</u> and <u>plastics</u>.

   1) <u>Wood screws</u> are used for, err... wood. As the screw is turned by a <u>screwdriver</u>, the thread (the twisty bit around the outside of the screw) pulls it into the wood. Different types of <u>head</u> are available for different jobs, e.g. <u>round</u>, <u>countersunk</u>, <u>slotted</u> and <u>cross</u> heads.

2) <u>Self-tapping</u> screws have <u>hardened threads</u> and are designed to <u>cut their own threaded holes</u> in hard materials such as <u>metals</u> and <u>hard plastics</u>.

head

thread shank

3) <u>Machine screws</u> have a straight <u>shank</u> and are used with <u>washers</u> and <u>nuts</u>. Heads vary (round, countersunk, etc.).

4) <u>Bolts</u> are similar to machine screws. They have <u>square</u>, <u>round</u> or <u>hexagonal</u> heads and are tightened with <u>spanners</u>.

Standard joke components — an Englishman, an Irishman...

Standard components are all over the place, the staples in this book, the screws holding together the chair you're sat on and the buttons on your clothes. Amazing — OK, so it's quite boring actually...

Standard Components

...And So Are Knock-Down Fittings

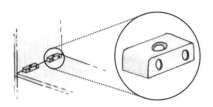

1) These are blocks, brackets (plastic or metal) and other fittings which enable furniture to be assembled and taken apart again easily.

2) They're used instead of traditional joints, and are very fast to use, but are nowhere near as strong as glued joints.

3) Most types are assembled with screwdrivers or Allen keys.

4) They're usually used for cheap 'flat-pack' furniture.

Rivets are Standard Components that Join Sheet Metal

1) A rivet is a metal peg with a head on one end. Rivets are mostly used for joining pieces of metal.

standard rivets

2) A hole is drilled through both pieces of metal and the rivet is inserted with a set (hammer-like tool). The head is held against the metal whilst the other end is flattened and shaped into another head with a hammer.

3) 'Pop' (or 'blind') rivets are now very common. They can be used where there is only access to one side of the material (hence 'blind' rivet). It's a fast and easy method of joining sheet metal. Here's how it works:

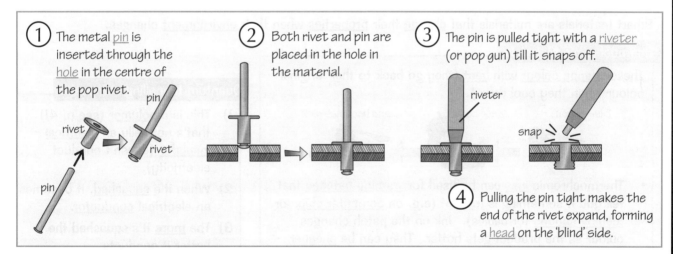

① The metal pin is inserted through the hole in the centre of the pop rivet.

② Both rivet and pin are placed in the hole in the material.

③ The pin is pulled tight with a riveter (or pop gun) till it snaps off.

④ Pulling the pin tight makes the end of the rivet expand, forming a head on the 'blind' side.

Practice Questions

1) a) What is a standard component?
   b) Why is it a good idea for manufacturers to use standard components?
   c) Name three standard components used in the textile industry.

2) Jim is using screws to join the wood in his product together.
   a) What type of screws should Jim use?
   b) List three different kinds of screw head.

3) a) What are knock-down fittings?
   b) Where are knock-down fittings often used?

4) What are rivets used for?

New Materials

Believe it or not, but <u>quantum tunnelling composites</u> do actually exist outside of sci-fi shows...

New Materials *Have New Useful* Properties

The development of new materials with different and useful <u>properties</u> has meant that designers can come up with <u>better products</u> to meet customers' needs. Here are <u>two</u> examples:

1) **Cornstarch polymers** are made from <u>maize</u> (sweetcorn). They're <u>renewable materials</u> (you can always grow more maize).

2) They're <u>biodegradable</u> — when you've finished with them they'll <u>rot</u> away in a compost heap.

3) They're sometimes used as a more <u>sustainable</u> alternative to normal <u>plastics</u> — this <u>saves</u> finite resources like <u>oil</u>, and creates less need for <u>landfill waste</u>.

4) They can be made in a <u>clear</u>, <u>flexible</u> form for sandwich packaging, disposable cups, etc.

Precious metal clay is a new material that contains <u>particles</u> of <u>metal</u> (often silver) in a <u>binding material</u>. It's used to make <u>jewellery</u>.

① The clay is really <u>easy to work with</u> — you can <u>cut it</u>, <u>roll it</u> and <u>shape it</u> like <u>modelling clay</u>.

② When the clay is <u>heated</u>, the binder burns away, and the <u>metal fuses together</u> to create a <u>solid metal object</u>.

③ After it's heated, you can <u>solder</u> and <u>polish</u> it too.

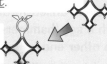

'Smart' *Materials* React to Their Environment

Smart materials are materials that <u>change</u> their <u>properties</u> when their <u>environment</u> changes.

Thermochromic Materials

These <u>change colour</u> with <u>heat</u> (they go back to their original colour when they cool down).

Blue spoon...   ...gets hot...   ...and becomes pink.

• Thermochromic <u>inks</u> can be used for <u>warning patches</u> that tell you if something is <u>too hot</u> (e.g. on <u>computer chips</u> or <u>feeding spoons</u> for babies). Ink on the patch changes colour as the product gets hotter. They can be <u>cheaper</u> and <u>more reliable</u> than electronic heat warnings.

• Thermochromic <u>dyes</u> can be <u>impregnated</u> into <u>textiles</u>, e.g. <u>babygrows</u> can be made that show when a <u>child</u> has a <u>temperature</u>.

Quantum tunnelling composite

1) This is a <u>polymer</u> (see p. 41) that's normally an <u>electrical insulator</u> (doesn't conduct electricity).

2) When it's <u>squashed</u>, it becomes an electrical <u>conductor</u>.

3) The <u>more</u> it's squashed the <u>better</u> it conducts.

4) They're <u>inserted</u> into <u>textiles</u> to <u>control</u> integrated electronics (see next page).

Percy wished his glasses were made of nitinol.

Shape memory alloys (e.g. Nitinol™)

1) These can be easily shaped when <u>cool</u>, but return to a 'remembered' shape when heated above a certain temperature.

2) So if your glasses are made of nitinol and you accidentally <u>bend</u> them, you can just pop them into a bowl of hot water and they'll <u>jump</u> back <u>into shape</u>.

Smart and modern — well, I don't like to brag...

Think you're made of smart material then... well cover up this page and see if you can write it all out.

New Materials

Nanomaterials are made from nanoparticles — which are really really really really tiny lumps of material — so tiny that you could fit about a thousand of them into the width of one of these hairs.

Nanomaterials Have Useful Properties

Nanoparticles of a material often have different properties from the 'normal' material — that's why nanomaterials can be very useful.
They're used to make products such as:

1) Self-cleaning glass for windows — the glass has a coating of nanoparticles that cause dirt to break down so it can be easily washed off by rainwater.

2) Self-cleaning fabrics — fabric is coated with nanoparticles that will resist and break down dirt and stains.

3) Antibacterial fabrics — by attaching nanoparticles of silver to fabrics they can kill bacteria. These fabrics have lots of medical uses, e.g. face masks and dressings. They can also be used to make anti-bacterial toys and odour-free socks.

When incorporated into fabrics the nanoparticles are so small that they don't change the feel of the fabric (unlike conventional finishes, see page 47).

Integrated Electronics Are Built-in Circuits

1) Electronic devices can be incorporated into a product design — this is known as integrated electronics.

2) It's commonly done in textile design, where devices like mp3 players can be incorporated into things like clothing and bags. These devices are often operated with quantum tunnelling composite switches. These are washable and so can be permanently attached to the product.

3) Other applications include putting sensors in clothes that monitor heart rate and blood pressure.

Practice Questions

1) A supermarket chain claims that they package most of their food with cornstarch.
Describe the potential environmental benefits of using cornstarch.

2) Najoud has a ring made from precious metal clay.
Outline how the ring would have been made.

3) Paul is designing a can for his Dandelion and Burdock drink.
He wants to use a smart material to make a label that will show when the drink is too warm.
a) What is a smart material?
b) Suggest which smart material he could use for his label, and describe how it would work.

4) What is a nanomaterial?

5) Bill has designed a new toy. Suggest how he might have used a nanomaterial in his design to make the product safer for children.

6) Arthur wants to incorporate an mp3 player into his coat using integrated electronics.
a) How might the mp3 player be operated?
b) Give another use of integrated electronics.

Safety

No, don't turn over — you really need to read this stuff...

Safety is Essential when You Make a Product

Wear the Right Protective Clothing

1) With hazardous materials wear a face mask or goggles and protective gloves. If there are fumes you should make sure there's enough ventilation. Use a dust extractor if the process produces dust.

2) If the material is hot, wear protective gloves and an apron. For some jobs, e.g. welding, you should also wear a face shield.

Be Careful with Tools and Machinery

1) By law, workers must always use safe working practices for tools and machinery.

2) When you're working with tools and machinery, make sure you have your sleeves rolled back, ties tucked in or taken off, apron strings tucked in and long hair tied back.

3) Never leave any machines unattended while switched on.

4) Never use a machine unless you've been taught how to.

5) Know how to switch off machines in an emergency.

6) Don't change parts (e.g. drill bits) on a machine until you've isolated it from the mains.

Handle Materials and Waste Sensibly

1) Choose your materials sensibly — only use hazardous materials when absolutely necessary.

2) Make sure materials are safe to handle, e.g file down rough edges before starting work.

3) Store materials safely, e.g. keep foods that could go off (fresh meat, etc.) in a fridge at 0–5 °C. Keep flammable liquids away from naked flames and red-hot heating elements.

4) Dispose of waste properly so that it doesn't harm the environment.

Risk Assessments are Important

1) A risk assessment is when you identify potential hazards and put precautions in place to minimise the risk, e.g. placing warning signs on machines, or erecting barriers and guards.

2) Here's part of a risk assessment for using a pillar drill.

3) Risk assessments are carried out at all stages of production:

- During the design process risk assessments are carried out on the product to assess potential risks to the end user. (See the next page for more on this.)

- Manufacturers do risk assessments covering the materials, chemicals and equipment that workers will have to use during manufacture.

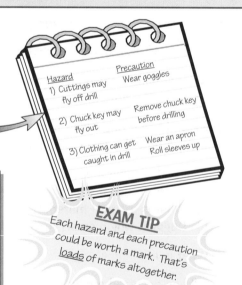

Hazard	Precaution
1) Cuttings may fly off drill	Wear goggles
2) Chuck key may fly out	Remove chuck key before drilling
3) Clothing can get caught in drill	Wear an apron Roll sleeves up

EXAM TIP
Each hazard and each precaution could be worth a mark. That's loads of marks altogether.

Careful — you could have someone's eye out with that...

The Health and Safety at Work Act says that employers are legally responsible for the health and safety of their employees. It also says that workers must work safely — use safety equipment provided, etc.

Safety

Think About the Consumer — Design Safe Products

Designers and manufacturers have a <u>moral</u> and <u>legal responsibility</u>
to make their products as <u>safe</u> as possible for the user.

> According to the <u>Consumer Protection Act</u>:
>
> 1) It's the <u>designer's</u> responsibility to make sure that their product
>   doesn't present an <u>unnecessary</u> danger to the consumer.
>
> 2) It's the <u>manufacturer's</u> responsibility to make sure that the product:
>   • isn't <u>contaminated</u> by harmful chemicals during its production,
>   • has got the right <u>safety warnings</u> on it,
>   • is <u>recalled</u> if it's found to be dangerous.
>
> If they <u>don't</u> do this, they could be in <u>trouble</u> if someone hurts themselves.

You won't <u>always</u> be able to avoid potential harm — e.g. a round-ended chisel would be very safe, but it wouldn't do its job.

You Can Carry Out Tests to Ensure Safety

Even in school, there are things you can do to make sure the product you're designing is <u>safe</u>.

1) <u>Research your materials</u> carefully and <u>test them</u> to make sure they're suitable,
   e.g. see how far they'll bend, check whether they catch fire easily, etc.

2) Use <u>standard components</u> (see p. 58-59) wherever you can, because these have already been
   tested by the manufacturer — this helps make sure that safety standards are met.

3) Make <u>prototypes</u> and carry out real life <u>simulations</u>, e.g. if you're making a cot, check that a
   toddler's finger can't get trapped in the gaps between the bars (using a metal rod of about the
   same width as a toddler's finger, for example).

4) Get <u>electrical</u> items <u>PAT tested</u> (PAT stands for Portable Appliance Test).
   The test makes sure that portable electric products won't hurt anyone
   if used properly. School technicians can sometimes do this.

5) You can test products using <u>CAD</u> software (e.g. SolidWorks®). If you've selected the <u>right</u>
   <u>materials</u>, you can simulate <u>stress tests</u>, such as how well a product will stand up to an impact.

Practice Questions

1) a) What <u>protective equipment</u> should you wear if you are handling <u>hot</u> materials or equipment?
   b) What additional precaution should you take if you're making a lot of <u>dust</u>?

2) Terry is going to <u>tie dye</u> his T-shirt using a <u>chemical</u> dye that is <u>toxic</u> and gives off harmful fumes.
   Suggest some <u>precautions</u> he should take and explain why they are needed.

3) List four health and safety procedures that should be followed when using <u>machinery</u>,
   e.g. a sewing machine.

4) When are <u>risk assessments</u> carried out?

5) Brian works for a toy company designing children's <u>teddy bears</u>. A manufacturer follows one of
   Brian's designs to produce a batch of teddy bears. Unfortunately they turn out to be unsafe
   because children can pull their eyes off easily.
   a) Who is legally <u>responsible</u> for this problem — Brian or the manufacturer of the teddy bear?
      Explain your answer.
   b) Suggest how the problem could have been spotted before the teddy bear was manufactured.

64

Quality

People sometimes have <u>different ideas</u> about what makes a good, <u>high-quality</u> product. For example, I think my thigh-high, leopard-print boots are <u>ace</u> — but some people have told me they're a bit trashy.

Quality Can Mean Lots of Things

1) To judge if a product is good, it should be compared against <u>several different criteria</u>, e.g. <u>cost</u>, use of <u>materials</u>, how easy it is to <u>use</u>, what it <u>looks</u> like, etc.

2) 'High quality' <u>doesn't</u> just mean <u>put together well</u>. For example a sports car might be well made, look great and go really fast, but it could <u>cost a fortune</u> to buy and run...

3) ...so lots of people might think a <u>less flashy</u> but more <u>fuel-efficient</u> car like this one is a <u>better quality</u> product.

Some Organisations Judge Products to Help Customers

1) There are some <u>independent groups</u> (they're not funded by manufacturers) that <u>judge products</u> and give feedback on them to help consumers.

2) For example, Which? tests products (different washing machines, say) and gives them <u>scores</u> for things like ease of use, running costs, etc. They publish the results in their magazine, Which? and on the internet, so people can compare products and see what's right for them.

There are Laws to Protect Consumers

Companies who produce <u>unsafe</u> or <u>unreliable</u> products have probably broken one of these <u>laws</u>:

1) The <u>Consumer Protection From Unfair Trading Regulations</u> ensure that any claims made about a product (e.g. that it is hard-wearing, long-lasting, waterproof) must be true.

2) The <u>General Product Safety Regulations</u> state that nobody can put a product on the market unless it's <u>safe</u>.

3) The <u>Sale Of Goods Act</u> ensures that products perform as you would reasonably expect and that goods last a reasonable length of time.

4) <u>Furniture and Furnishings (Fire Safety) Regulations</u> cover upholstered furniture and cushions, etc. to ensure that they don't catch fire easily and don't give off really toxic fumes when they burn.

There are Standards For Many Products

1) There are various <u>organisations</u> that set <u>standards</u> of safety, quality or design for certain types of product. Products that meet these standards are usually <u>labelled</u> to show this — see page 26.

2) The <u>British Standards Institution (BSI)</u> is one example of this kind of standards institution. Another example is the <u>British Toy and Hobby Association</u> (BTHA).

3) The <u>International Organisation for Standardisation (ISO)</u> also issues <u>certificates</u> to organisations that meet international standards of quality. (See the next page.)

Never judge a book by its cover — unless it's a consumer test...

To make a <u>good quality</u> product, you need to know what that means for the <u>customer</u> and how to go about <u>checking</u> your work to make sure that <u>standards</u> are being met. It's the same in <u>industry</u>.

Quality

To make sure their products are high quality, manufacturers have a quality assurance system in place.

Quality Assurance (QA) is an Overall System

1) Quality assurance involves having good staff training, procedures for checking the quality of materials and systems for keeping machinery maintained.

2) It also includes quality control checks throughout the manufacturing process — see below.

3) So when you're planning a manufacturing system (for your project or in the exam), remember to work in quality checks at every stage. This will help your product to:

> 1) do the job it's designed to do
> 2) meet the standards set down by the relevant institutions
> 3) keep the customer happy
> 4) be manufactured consistently

4) Teamwork is important for quality assurance. A quality circle is a group of workers who meet to discuss problems and come up with ideas for solving them.

5) Companies that do QA well are awarded ISO 9000 — an international standard of quality management.

Quality Control Means Checking Components

Quality control means testing samples of components or finished products to check that they meet the manufacturing specification.

For example, a greetings card might be tested to make sure all the images are printed clearly, the edges are cut accurately, the card is folded in the right place, the text is straight and it plays the right tune, etc.

When a component or product is checked for accuracy, it must be within the tolerance given in the manufacturing specification (usually as upper and lower limits).

For example, if a component is supposed to be 200 mm wide ± 3 mm then a width of 118 mm would be OK but a width of 204 mm would not be OK.

Practice Questions

1) John wants to buy a new car.
Suggest how he could get some independent advice about the quality of various different models.

2) Katie is designing a bed. She is assessing whether her product will break any laws. Which laws cover the following things?
a) Whether the bed will last a long time.
b) Whether the mattress will give off toxic fumes if it catches fire.

3) What is a quality control check?

4) What is ISO 9000?

5) Derek is cropping photos to a size of 15 cm by 10 cm. The tolerance is ±0.4 cm.
a) What's the biggest the photos can be?
b) What's the smallest the photos can be?

Ethics and Environmental Issues

When you design and make a product, you should think about the impact it will have on the environment.

Sustainable Design is Better for the Environment

Sustainability means not causing permanent damage to the environment and not using up finite resources (ones that'll run out eventually). How sustainable a design is depends on:

What materials are used, for example:
- do they come from renewable resources — or finite ones?
- are they recyclable or biodegradable — or will the used product just be chucked into landfill?

See Section 4 for more on materials.

The processes used to make the product, for example:
- does the process need lots of energy?
- does it create lots of waste or pollution?

Sustainability also depends on the design itself — how long-lasting and efficient the product is...

Some Products Aren't Designed to Last

1) Some products are designed to become obsolete (useless) quickly. E.g. a disposable razor becomes blunt after a few uses and its blade can't be sharpened or changed. This is built-in obsolescence.

2) Products with very up-to-the-minute designs become obsolete quickly because they go out of fashion. For example, people often replace their mobile phone when a new, fancier model comes out.

3) Built-in obsolescence is generally bad for the environment — because more materials and energy are used to make replacement products.

4) Products can be designed to last. This involves making the product durable, and designing it so that parts can be maintained and repaired or replaced.

For example, some bicycle chains have a 'quick-release' link so that you can remove the chain to clean and oil it. (Though the owner of this bike obviously didn't bother.) And when the chain eventually wears out you don't need to buy a whole new bike — you just replace the chain.

Products have a Carbon Footprint

1) A carbon footprint is the amount of greenhouse gases (carbon dioxide, methane and other gases) released by making or using something. All products all have a carbon footprint...

2) ...because carbon dioxide is released when they're made, transported and used. That's because fossil fuels are burned to provide the energy for these processes, and this emits carbon dioxide.

3) So the more energy that's needed to make something, the bigger its carbon footprint.

4) A product's carbon footprint is also affected by the distance it travels from where it's made to where it's used (this is called product miles). For food products it's often called food miles. Clever.

5) Making products so that they use energy efficiently could reduce their carbon footprint. Appliances often have energy efficiency ratings, e.g. an A-rated fridge is more efficient than a D-rated one.

My carbon footprint's a size 6...

Some companies try to reduce the damage their carbon footprint does by carbon offsetting. E.g. they might plant trees — as the trees grow they absorb some of the carbon dioxide from the atmosphere.

Ethics and Environmental Issues

You Need to Know the 6 Rs

The 6 Rs are some things to think about when you're designing, to help <u>reduce the impact</u> your products have on the <u>environment</u> and make the whole process more <u>sustainable</u>. There are things for consumers to think about too.

1) REPAIR It's better to <u>fix</u> things <u>instead</u> of <u>throwing</u> them away.
E.g. <u>repairing</u> a mobile phone can sometimes cost the <u>same</u>
as buying a <u>new</u> one, but is better for the <u>environment</u>.
Manufacturers can still make a profit by selling <u>replacement parts</u>.

2) REUSE Customers can <u>extend a product's life</u> by passing it on
or using it again. Some people <u>reuse</u> products for <u>other</u>
<u>purposes</u> e.g. using an old car tyre to make a swing.

*Sonia found a new use for
her old toilet brush*

3) RECYCLE Recycling uses <u>less energy</u> than obtaining <u>new</u> materials,
e.g. by extracting metal. Products made from more than
one material should ideally be <u>easy to separate</u> into
recyclable stuff — clear 'recycle' <u>labelling</u> helps with this.

4) RETHINK You should <u>think</u> about your design carefully — you might
be able to <u>make</u> the product in a <u>different way</u>, e.g. a
radio that you <u>wind up</u> instead of running off batteries.

5) REDUCE Making <u>long-lasting</u>, <u>durable</u> products like
<u>rechargeable batteries</u> reduces the <u>number</u>
of products customers need to buy. It also
means that manufacturers can <u>cut down</u> on
<u>energy</u> use and <u>transport</u>.

EMMELINE WATKINS/
SCIENCE PHOTO LIBRARY

6) REFUSE You can <u>refuse</u> to buy a product if you think it's <u>wasteful</u> —
e.g. if it has lots of <u>unnecessary packaging</u>, has travelled <u>long distances</u>
round the world to the UK, or will be <u>inefficient</u> or costly to run.

Practice Questions

1) What does the term <u>finite resource</u> mean?

2) a) What is meant by <u>built-in obsolescence</u>?
   b) Why is built-in obsolescence usually bad for the environment?

3) Julie is designing a children's <u>toy truck</u>.
   Suggest some features the truck could have to make it <u>long-lasting</u>.

4) a) What is a <u>carbon footprint</u>?
   b) What is meant by <u>product miles</u>?
   c) John lives in Birmingham. He has bought a very energy-efficient fridge that was made in
      Germany. His neighbour's fridge is less energy-efficient but was made in Birmingham.
      Whose fridge do you think has a lower carbon footprint? Explain your answer.

5) Bob is designing some disposable plastic cutlery.
   Suggest how he could use the <u>6 Rs</u> to reduce the cutlery's impact on the environment.

68

Ethics and Environmental Issues

Every part of a product's life cycle has some impact on the environment.

Which Materials You Use Matters

1) Some materials are toxic, e.g. some paints and varnishes give off fumes called VOCs (volatile organic compounds) which can be harmful to humans and also contribute to global warming.

2) Many materials are made from finite resources. For example, there's only a limited amount of metal ores in the Earth's crust. Most plastics are made from crude oil, which will eventually run out.

 It's better to use materials from renewable resources — ones that are replaced naturally as fast as we use them up. For example, pine from well-managed plantations is quite a sustainable choice. (But if the timber has to be transported a long way that'll probably use up a lot of fossil fuels.) Natural fibres used for textiles (e.g. cotton) are all renewable.

Using recycled materials means that fewer new resources are needed, and often less energy is used. For example, recycling old food cans takes much less energy than mining and processing new metal.

3) What materials are used also affects how the product can be disposed of when its useful life is over...

Product Disposal is Important Too

1) Every product eventually comes to the end of its life — even a 'bag for life' that can be re-used many times will eventually wear out. So you have to get rid of stuff somehow.

2) Some materials are biodegradable — they will rot away naturally (in a compost heap, say). Wood and paper are biodegradable and so are some new plastics.

3) Many materials are recyclable. Paper, glass and most metals are all easy to recycle. Plastics can be recycled but it's expensive, and their structure breaks down a bit during the process, so you can't keep doing it.

4) Many products carry symbols to tell you if they're recyclable.

5) Products made from lots of components and several different materials are awkward to recycle, because it's fiddly to separate all the parts before you can recycle them.

For example, many fruit juice cartons are made mainly of card...

...but they also have a foil lining and a plastic top.

This book is recyclable — but keep it till after the exams...

Folk used to just chuck their rubbish into massive holes in the ground (landfill). But that's not pretty or sustainable — it causes pollution (when toxic chemicals leak) and eventually we'd just run out of space.

Section 5 — Social and Environmental Issues

Ethics and Environmental Issues

Recycling has to be Collected, Sorted and Processed

1) Consumers often have to sort their rubbish for recycling into boxes that are collected by the local council. Most towns also have recycling centres with 'banks' for bottles, cardboard, etc.

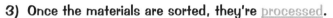

2) Sometimes the sorting can be done by machine. For example, magnets are used to separate different sorts of metals and infrared light is used to sort plastics.

3) Once the materials are sorted, they're processed.

- Water is added to paper to make it into paper pulp, which is then de-inked. The pulp is then made into new paper. Most newspapers are made partly with recycled paper.
- Glass and metal are crushed, heated up and melted — then poured into moulds to make new stuff.

> Recycling won't solve all the world's environmental problems though. For starters it uses energy, which usually comes from burning fossil fuels:
> - waste has to be transported to processing centres in lorries
> - processing the materials also needs energy — usually heat and electricity.

Companies Have a Social Responsibility

1) Designing and making new products can have social benefits, e.g. bringing new jobs to an area.

2) But companies also have a responsibility to make sure no one's health or way of life is harmed by making the products.

3) The fair trade movement tries to make sure that workers (e.g. people making handicrafts or working in manufacturing) in developing countries are paid fairly and have good working conditions.

Fairtrade Certification

The FAIRTRADE Mark is used on products that meet international Fairtrade standards, e.g. bananas, cocoa. It's the consumer's guarantee that producers have been paid an agreed and stable price which covers the cost of sustainable production.

Practice Questions

1) Give an example of a renewable material and explain why it's renewable.

2) What does biodegradable mean?

3) Gilbert has bought a model train. Some of its parts are made from plastics, some are metal and some are made from wood.
   a) Do you think the model train would be easy to recycle? Explain your answer.
   b) The wooden parts of the train have been varnished. Suggest a possible environmental impact of this process.

4) Recycling materials uses up energy. Explain why.

5) Ben buys some rice that has a label showing the FAIRTRADE Mark. What does this mean?

Tools

There are a huge range of tools out there to <u>cut</u>, <u>shape</u> and <u>form</u> materials.

Materials Can be Cut Using Hand Tools...

Saws have to be kept sharp, either by <u>sharpening</u> or <u>replacing</u> the blade.

<u>Saws</u> are the main cutting tools. There are <u>different saws</u> for different materials:

Panel saw — for wood

Tenon saw — for wood

Hacksaw — for metals and plastics

Coping saw — for cutting curves in wood or plastic

<u>Rough edges</u> from sawing can be tidied up by <u>sanding</u> or <u>planing</u> for <u>wood</u>, <u>filing</u> for <u>metal</u> or <u>buffing</u> for <u>plastic</u>.

...and Machine Tools

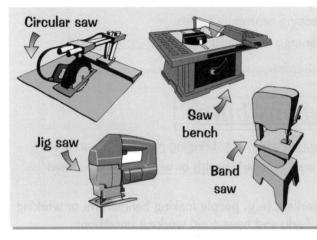
Circular saw

Saw bench

Jig saw

Band saw

1) <u>Circular saws</u> and <u>saw benches</u> have round blades and are used to cut <u>wood</u> and boards like <u>plywood</u>. They make <u>straight cuts only</u>.

2) <u>Band saws</u> have blades in long flexible loops. They come in different widths and can make <u>straight</u> or <u>curved</u> cuts. Band saws are usually used on <u>wood</u> but special blades can be bought to cut <u>plastics</u> and <u>softer metals</u>.

3) A <u>jig saw</u> has <u>interchangeable blades</u> and <u>variable speeds</u>. You can make <u>straight</u> or <u>curved</u> cuts in all materials, but it's quite <u>slow</u>.

Drills Make Holes (no kidding...)

1) To help you drill in the right place, you can make a <u>pilot hole</u> first using a <u>bradawl</u>.
   Bradawls can only be used on wood and plastic. You'd use a <u>centre punch</u> for metal.

2) Depending on how hard the material is, you can do the actual drilling with a <u>brace</u>, a <u>hand drill</u> or a <u>power drill</u> (e.g. a <u>pillar drill</u>).

3) All drills work by rotating a <u>drill bit</u> against the material.

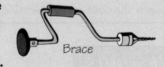
Brace

Hand drill

Pillar drill

<u>Twist bits</u> are used to drill <u>small holes</u> in wood, metal or plastic.
<u>High speed steel</u> (HSS) twist bits are used on metals and plastics.

<u>Flat bits</u> are used on <u>wood</u> to drill <u>large</u> flat-bottomed holes.

<u>Countersink bits</u> widen the <u>opening</u> to an <u>existing hole</u>, allowing <u>screw heads</u> to sit <u>flat</u> on the <u>surface</u>.

You need to be well drilled in this stuff for the exam...

There's nothing here to blow your mind — <u>saws</u> cut stuff up and <u>drills</u> make holes. Easy.
Make sure you don't skimp when you're learning the <u>details</u> though — it's all important stuff.

Tools

Materials Can be Shaped Using Hand Tools

1) <u>Wood chisels</u> come in different profiles for making different shapes. You hit them with a <u>mallet</u>.

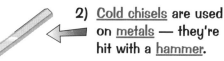
2) <u>Cold chisels</u> are used on <u>metals</u> — they're hit with a <u>hammer</u>.

3) <u>Gougers</u> are chisels with a <u>curved cutting edge</u> — they're used for <u>sculpting</u>.

4) <u>Bench planes</u> have angled blades that <u>shave</u> off <u>thin layers</u> of material. They're used to shape <u>wood</u>.

5) <u>Files</u> have hundreds of small <u>teeth</u> to cut away at a material. Different 'cuts' of file are used for different processes — <u>rough cuts</u> are for <u>removing material</u> and <u>fine cuts</u> are for final smoothing.

triangular file
hand file
half round file
flat file

Files come in different <u>profiles</u> to make different shapes. Files are usually used on <u>metals</u> and <u>plastics</u>, but there are some with very coarse teeth called <u>cabinet rasps</u> for use on <u>wood</u>. <u>Needle files</u> are used for <u>fine</u> and <u>detailed</u> work.

Materials Can Also be Shaped Using Machine Tools

A <u>planer</u> and <u>thicknesser</u> (either separate or both in a single machine) are used to <u>remove material</u> from the surface of pieces of wood to give a <u>consistent cross section</u>.

A <u>milling machine</u> is used to remove <u>one thin layer of material at a time</u> to produce the required size or shape. It can also be used to make a surface absolutely <u>flat</u>. Milling machines produce a very <u>accurate</u> finish.

A <u>bench grinder</u> contains <u>abrasive wheels</u> of different grades (coarse to smooth). It's used to <u>remove metal</u> for <u>shaping</u> or <u>finishing</u> purposes, as well as for <u>sharpening</u> edged tools such as chisels.

<u>Lathes</u> are used to <u>cut</u> and <u>shape</u> materials to produce <u>rounded</u> objects, e.g. chair legs. The material is <u>held</u> and <u>rotated</u> by the lathe and the <u>turning tool</u> or <u>cutting bit</u> is pressed onto the material.

Practice Questions

1) What type of saw is used for cutting <u>metals</u>?
2) What is a <u>coping saw</u> used for?
3) Phil wants to make a <u>pilot hole</u> before he drills a hole for a screw in a piece of wood. Suggest what tool he could use to make the pilot hole.
4) Name two types of <u>drill bit</u> and say what they're used for.
5) Paul wants to remove some shavings of wood from a table he is making. Suggest a <u>hand tool</u> and a <u>power tool</u> that he could use to do this.

Forming and Bending

When you're making a product, you often need to <u>change the shape</u> of a material.
The way you do this depends on the material you're using.

Sheet Metals Can be Folded

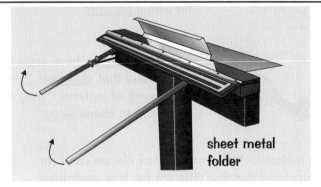

sheet metal folder

1) You can use a <u>sheet metal folder</u> to shape <u>sheet metals</u> such as aluminium and tin plate.
2) The outline of the product, e.g. a box, is marked out and cut from a <u>flat</u> sheet of metal.
3) You <u>feed the metal in</u> flat, make one fold then move the material through for the next fold.
4) Corners can then be <u>joined</u> using rivets (page 59), or by soldering, brazing, etc.

Most Metals Need to be Heated Before Bending

1) Some <u>thin</u> pieces of metal can be bent cold on a <u>jig</u> or <u>former</u> — they can be <u>cold worked</u>.
2) <u>Thicker</u> or harder metals have to be heated or <u>annealed</u> first (see page 39) and allowed to cool.
3) This makes them soft enough to bend easily, but the annealing process might have to be repeated as bending makes them go <u>hard</u> again — this is known as '<u>work hardening</u>'.

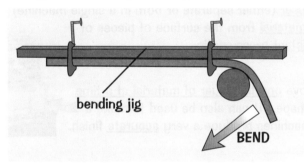

bending jig

BEND

Metal would have been heated and bent to make this shovel.

Iron and Steel are Forged

1) Metal, especially <u>iron</u> and <u>steel</u>, can be heated in a <u>forge</u>.

2) A forge is a fire with <u>air</u> blown into the middle of it to produce a very hot flame.
3) When the metal's hot enough to have softened sufficiently, it's taken out and hammered into shape on an <u>anvil</u>.
4) Hammering creates <u>stresses</u> in the metal, so it then needs to be <u>reheated</u> and <u>cooled slowly</u> to <u>smooth</u> it out.

You need to bend your brain around this page...

<u>Different materials</u> are bent using <u>different methods</u>. Makes sense really — you wouldn't really want to try forging plastic, for example. You'd just get a gooey puddle that wouldn't be much use for anything.

Section 6 — Processes and Manufacture

Forming and Bending

Wood and plastics can be bent and folded too.

Laminating *is* Gluing Thin Strips *of Material Together*

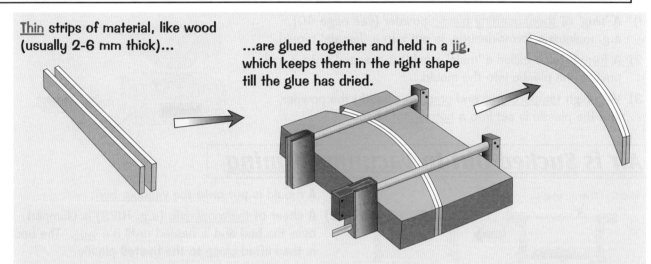

Thin strips of material, like wood (usually 2-6 mm thick)...

...are glued together and held in a jig, which keeps them in the right shape till the glue has dried.

Things that could be made this way include rocking chair runners, chair or table legs and roof beams.

Plastics *Can Also be Folded*

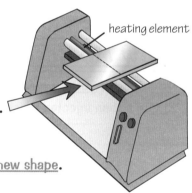

heating element

1) Line bending is ideal for use with acrylic sheets, e.g. for making picture frames and pencil holders, etc.

2) It can be done using a line bender or strip heater.

3) You rest the sheet on two bars and the element below heats the plastic. You just need to position the sheet carefully, so that the line you want to bend along is directly above the element.

4) Once the plastic is soft it can be bent. When it cools it will stay in its new shape.

Practice Questions

1) What machine could you use to make this metal magazine rack?

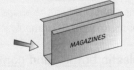
MAGAZINES

2) Sid wants to bend a thick piece of metal into the shape shown on the right.
   a) What does he need to do before he can bend the metal?
   b) Sketch a diagram to show how he can bend the metal using a bending jig.

3) What is an anvil used for?

4) a) Outline how laminating can be used to make bent wooden items.
   b) Suggest two products or components made by laminating wood.

5) Emma needs to fold a piece of acrylic for the picture frame she is making.
   a) Name a process she could use to fold the acrylic.
   b) Outline what happens during this process.

Casting and Moulding

There are plenty of ways to <u>mould</u> things — pressing, sucking and blowing just for starters.

Press Moulding Shapes Thermosetting Plastic

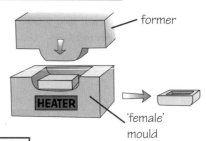

former

'female' mould

1) A 'slug' of <u>thermosetting plastic</u> powder (see page 40), e.g. melamine formaldehyde, is put into a '<u>female</u>' mould.

2) A <u>former</u> (also called a 'male' mould) is pressed onto it and pushes the plastic into the mould.

3) Very high <u>temperatures</u> and <u>pressures</u> liquify the powder, and the plastic is set into a <u>permanent</u> shape.

Air is Sucked Out In Vacuum Forming

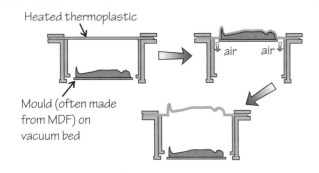

Heated thermoplastic

air   air

Mould (often made from MDF) on vacuum bed

1) A mould is put onto the <u>vacuum bed</u>.

2) A sheet of <u>thermoplastic</u> (e.g. **HIPS**) is clamped over the bed and is heated until it's <u>soft</u>. The bed is then lifted <u>close</u> to the heated plastic.

3) Air is <u>sucked</u> out from under the plastic, creating a <u>vacuum</u>. Air pressure from outside the mould forces the plastic onto the mould.

Blow Moulding... Well... Blows Air In

1) A tube of <u>softened plastic</u> (a <u>parison</u>) is inserted into a <u>solid mould</u>.

2) <u>Air</u> is then injected which forces the plastic to <u>expand</u> to the <u>shape</u> of the <u>mould</u>:

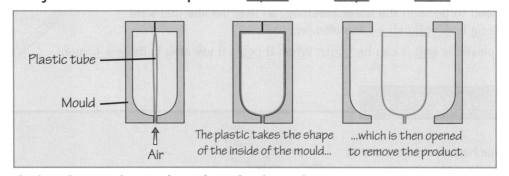

Plastic tube

Mould

Air

The plastic takes the shape of the inside of the mould...

...which is then opened to remove the product.

3) This method is often used to produce plastic <u>bottles</u> and <u>containers</u>.

Die Casting Also Uses a Mould

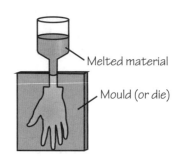

Melted material

Mould (or die)

1) Die casting is used to mould <u>metals</u> and <u>thermoplastics</u>.

2) The material is <u>melted</u> and poured into a <u>mould</u> (the 'die') which is in the shape of the product.

3) Some plastic resins can be <u>cold-poured</u> into moulds (without heating). They <u>harden</u> or <u>set</u> through a <u>chemical reaction</u>.

Don't eat this book — because this page is all mouldy...

In both <u>vacuum forming</u> and <u>injection moulding</u> (next page) the moulds must have <u>rounded corners</u> and be slightly <u>tapered</u> (sloped) at the sides — so that the finished product can be <u>released</u> from the mould.

Casting and Moulding

Injection Moulding Uses Pressure to Mould Plastics

1) This is similar to die casting, but the molten material is forced into a closed mould under pressure.
2) The moulds are often made from tool steel — so they're quite expensive.
3) The plastic is often melted using built-in heaters. A screw moves the plastic along towards the mould.
4) This is an industrial process which is usually automatic and continuous (see page 76).

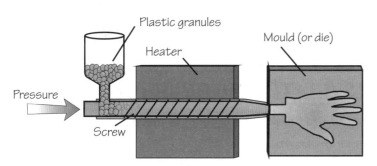

Plastics expert Brian had doubts about his new job.

Extrusion Produces Long, Continuous Strips

1) This process is very similar to injection moulding. It's used for some metals and thermoplastics.
2) The material is melted and forced under pressure through a die.
3) It produces long, continuous strips of the moulding exactly the same shape as the exit hole. It's used for products like plastic-covered wire, plastic and aluminium edgings, and also to make the parisons used in blow moulding.

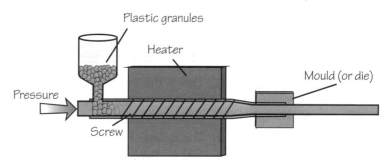

Practice Questions

1) a) What type of material is press moulding used to shape?
   b) Outline what happens during press moulding.

2) Describe the process of vacuum forming.

3) a) What moulding process is often used to make plastic bottles?
   b) Draw diagrams showing how this process could be used to make a plastic bottle.

4) a) What is a die?
   b) What types of materials can be moulded using die casting?

5) Peter is making a product using injection moulding.
   a) Suggest what type of material he is using.
   b) Outline the process of injection moulding.

6) Name two products that are made using extrusion moulding.

Scale of Production

Manufacturers use different production methods depending on the demand for the products they're making.

One-Off Production Makes One Product at a Time

1) One-off production is where you make "one-of-a-kind" products. Every item will be different, to meet a customer's exact requirements.
2) It's very labour intensive — it takes a lot of time to make each product. The workforce also needs to be highly skilled, so it's expensive.
3) One-off production is used for all sorts of things, from made-to-measure furniture to paintings.

Batch Production Makes A Certain Number of Products

1) Batch production is where a specific quantity (a batch) of a product is made.
2) Batches can be repeated as many times as necessary.
3) It's used to manufacture a load of one product (sofas, say), then a load of something a bit different (armchairs, for example).
4) The machinery and workforce used need to be flexible, so they can quickly change to making a batch of a different product.
5) The time between batches, when machines and tools may have to be set up differently or changed, is called down time. This wastes money because you're not making anything to sell.

Joe's flexibility impressed the interview panel.

Mass Production is Making Loads of the Same Product

1) This is the method you'd use to make thousands of identical products, like newspapers, magazines and cars. You'd only use this for a mass-market product — where loads of people want the same thing.
2) The different stages of production are broken down into simple repetitive tasks. Each worker only does a small part of the process, and the product moves further down an assembly line for each stage.
3) Mass production often uses expensive specialised equipment and CAD/CAM.
4) Recruitment is relatively easy — most of your staff don't need to be highly skilled.

Continuous Production is Non-Stop

1) Continuous production runs all the time, without interruption, 24 hours a day.
2) That's because it would be too expensive to keep stopping and restarting the process, especially if certain conditions need to be kept constant.
3) The equipment is built to make huge amounts of only one thing. This means it's expensive but it can be designed to be very efficient — so the cost per item is cheap.
4) Continuous production is used to make products such as aluminium foil, chemicals and oil.

Continuous production? Feels more like continuous revision...

So, products can be made as a unique one-off, in a group called a batch, in really massive numbers or in a continuous, never ending, keep going until the end of time way. And with keeping going in mind...

Scale of Production

Just-in-Time is Efficient but Needs Good Planning

In a just-in-time (JIT) system, the manufacturer gets the materials and components delivered as they're needed and uses them as soon as they're delivered. This has advantages:

1) It saves on space for storing materials — which saves money because you don't need to rent huge warehouses.
2) It means there's less money tied up in materials that aren't being used.
3) Unsold finished products don't pile up.

But it relies on materials and components being delivered on time and being fault free (because you don't have time to return faulty goods) — or else money can be lost.

The Scale of Production Affects the Product Design

Designers need to think about the scale of production when they're designing a product. For example:

A bed frame made by one-off production...

...might have a detailed design (e.g. intricate carvings). It's likely to be made from high quality materials and by a highly skilled craftsman. It would probably be designed to the specifications of the customer.

A bed frame made by batch production...

...is likely to have less detail in the design to make it easier to make a batch of identical products. Templates, jigs and moulds (p. 84) might be used to make the products consistent. It may be made from cheaper materials.

A bed frame made by mass production...

...is likely to have a basic design and be made from cheap materials. CAM machines (p. 85) might be used to quickly make large numbers of the product. It may be designed so that the customer can assemble it at home, e.g. using components that can be put together using basic tools.

Practice Questions

1) a) What type of production would you use to make a specific quantity of a product?
   b) Why, in that production method, do your workers and machinery need to be flexible?

 2) You've been asked to make 75 000 musical microwave ovens.
   a) What method of production will be best suited to this task?
   b) What is the advantage of this method when it comes to hiring workers?

3) Give an example of a product made using continuous production.

4) a) Briefly describe what a just-in-time system is.
   b) Why might a manufacturer use a just-in-time system?

5) Alonzo has designed a T-shirt. It sells well, so he decides to mass-produce it. Suggest how his production method might change when he increases production.

Manufacturing Systems and ICT

Systems and ICT may not sound like the most exciting things, but they're really important in manufacturing. And not as dull as you might think. But don't just take my word for it, read on and see what you reckon...

Commercial Manufacturing is a System

1) A system is a collection of parts and processes that work together in order to do a particular function.

2) Commercial manufacturing is a system — products are made as a result of a number of different steps.

3) Some commercial manufacturing processes may be made up of a group of subsystems. Each subsystem will make a different part of the product — these are then assembled to make the end product.

No... systems, not cisterns.

Systems Usually Have Three Parts

Manufacturing systems can be broken down into three elements — inputs, processes and outputs.

INPUT	PROCESS	OUTPUT
This is all of the materials, tools and equipment that you start off with.	This is what happens to the input to change it into an output, e.g. measuring, cutting and forming.	The output is the result of the system — in other words, the finished product.

Systems Improve the Manufacturing Process

Systems make manufacturing processes more efficient. They also help to make sure that the final product is top class — feedback loops are often built into them so you can do quality checks at each stage. How a system works can be shown as a flow chart, where the feedback loops are shown as diamond-shaped decision boxes.

For example: during the manufacturing process for pizzas, checks could be carried out for, say, the shape of the base or the amount of cheese on top. Pizzas that meet the set standard can move on to the next stage. Those that don't have to go back to the beginning of that stage. You can show this on a flow chart:

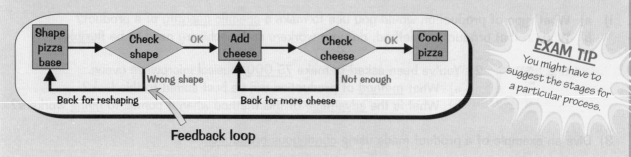

EXAM TIP
You might have to suggest the stages for a particular process.

You know the system by now — read, learn, cover, scribble...

Told you systems weren't too bad — and now you get to learn about ICT... There aren't many products made these days where ICT hasn't come in somewhere along the line — it's important stuff, so read on.

Manufacturing Systems and ICT

ICT Plays a Major Role in Manufacturing

ICT is used for a wide range of functions in manufacturing. For example:

Data Transfer

Data, e.g. design drawings, can be transferred electronically from one computer to another, anywhere in the world, using electronic data interchange (EDI). EDI is the direct transfer of information from one computer system to another, usually via the internet. This means that designing and manufacturing can be done in different locations — the designer's work can be electronically transferred to the manufacturing site. This is known as remote manufacturing.

Software Sharing

Software sharing is used to make computer software available to many computers at once. The programme can be put on a network — then all the computers connected to the network can access the programme without having to install it on each machine. It means that design files can be opened and edited on many computers. It's really useful for companies with large numbers of designers, or computers spread over a large area.

Stock Control

Manufacturers often use computerised stock control systems. When materials and components are used a computer can record how much stock is left. Stock control is particularly important in JIT production (see page 77) as it relies on stock being replaced when it's needed, but not before. It often uses computer systems that automatically order components when they're needed.

Video Conferencing

ICT can allow people in different places to hold meetings using live pictures and sound — this is known as video conferencing. Manufacturers can use video conferencing to improve communication with suppliers and designers. It can also be used to view manufacturing processes — the designer or client can watch the product being made without actually being there.

Practice Questions

1) What is a system?

2) What three things can manufacturing systems be broken down into?

3) How do systems improve the manufacturing process?

4) Linda is making a poster. She wants to use a guillotine to cut 5 cm off the top of a piece of paper. Draw a simple flow chart for this, including a feedback loop to show a quality check.

5) A designer has been asked to develop a series of posters and brochures to advertise a new holiday resort. Explain how ICT can be used to help develop the very best product.

Manufacturing Systems

Manufacturing systems need to run <u>effectively</u>, otherwise time and money will be wasted.

Manufacturing Should be <u>Systematic</u> and <u>Efficient</u>

For a manufacturing system to run <u>smoothly</u> and <u>efficiently</u>, it needs:

1) a trained and organised workforce

- Workers should have a specific <u>role</u> in a particular part of the manufacturing process.
- They need to be <u>trained</u> in the <u>skills</u> of their specific role.
- They also should be good at <u>communicating</u> with people involved in other parts of the process.

2) specialised buildings or workshops

- The workplace needs to be <u>suitable</u> for the particular manufacturing process.
- <u>Areas</u> should be designated for <u>different uses</u>, e.g. storage, finishing, packing.

3) good communication systems

- <u>Communication</u> is very important for the <u>smooth running</u> of the manufacturing process.
- <u>E-mail</u>, <u>telephones</u> and <u>fax machines</u> all help people communicate quickly, and allow information and data to be sent between departments.

Manufacturing systems also need quality control checks — see p. 64-65 for more on these.

4) organisation of tools, equipment and materials

- Materials need to be <u>ordered</u> at the <u>right time</u> — then when they arrive, they need to be stored in an <u>organised way</u>.
- Appropriate <u>tools</u> and <u>equipment</u> need to be used and they need to be <u>laid out</u> in a way that <u>speeds up</u> manufacture — see next page.

5) efficient design and production processes

- <u>Design</u> needs to be geared towards <u>mass production</u>, e.g. by using simple designs, and easily available and cheap materials.
- It also needs to consider the <u>best production processes</u>, e.g. in terms of cost and efficiency.

6) systems for disposing of waste

- Waste needs to be <u>disposed</u> of <u>safely</u>, with as little damage to the <u>environment</u> as possible.
- If possible, <u>recyclable</u> or <u>biodegradable</u> materials should be used.

7) risk assessment and safety procedures

- <u>Risk assessments</u> should be carried out to assess hazards and <u>minimise the risk</u> to workers.
- Workers should follow health and safety <u>guidelines</u> and <u>procedures</u>.

Systematic and efficient — just like your revision needs to be...

There you are — the <u>manufacturing system</u> divided up into <u>seven easy chunks</u>. Get these right and you'll be making products more smoothly than... um, a very smooth thing. And getting top marks too.

Manufacturing Systems

The <u>layout</u> of things can really affect how <u>efficient</u> a manufacturing system is.

Efficient <u>Workplace</u> Layouts Speed Up <u>Manufacture</u>

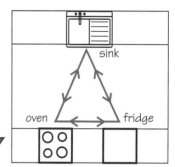

1) Having stages of an <u>assembly line</u> (p. 76) near to each other can prevent people wasting <u>time</u> and <u>energy</u> walking between different areas — e.g. the finishing area should be near the packaging area when making food products.

2) In other words, areas should <u>follow on</u> from each other in the order of the manufacturing process.

3) Many machines or processes in a <u>closed loop</u> that produce a product are also called a <u>manufacturing cell</u>.

4) When designing <u>kitchens</u>, a <u>working triangle</u> is often used. This is a plan of where to put the fridge, cooker and sink so that workers don't have to walk far between them.

A Good <u>Layout</u> can Also Help with <u>Quality</u>

Apart from helping to save <u>time</u>, the <u>layout</u> of a workplace can also help to ensure <u>quality</u>.

1) <u>Finishing</u> areas for tasks like painting or varnishing <u>shouldn't</u> be put next to <u>dirty</u> or <u>dusty</u> work areas.

2) Preventing products <u>travelling</u> a long way can reduce possible <u>damage</u>. Finished packaged products should be placed near the <u>dispatch</u> area (where goods leave from) so they don't have to travel all through the factory and risk getting knocked or bumped.

3) By carefully planning how to <u>store</u> materials and products you can fit <u>more</u> into a warehouse.

Materials <u>and Equipment</u> Layout is Important too

1) <u>Controls</u> for <u>machinery</u> should be <u>easy to reach</u> — stop buttons might need to be reached quickly in an emergency.

2) Controls should also be simple and <u>clearly labelled</u> to save time and confusion.

3) Materials should be organised in a <u>logical way</u>. For example, different sized planks of wood or bars of metal should be stacked neatly in <u>sections</u> and <u>labelled</u> so that workers can easily find the materials they need.

4) Systems like <u>barcodes</u> can be handy for organising materials, and for keeping an eye on <u>stock levels</u>.

5) Materials should also be <u>stored</u> carefully — e.g. raw meat shouldn't be stored next to cooked meat to <u>avoid contamination</u>.

Practice Questions

1) List <u>four</u> things a manufacturing system needs in order to run <u>efficiently</u>.

2) Describe how the layout of a workplace can be designed to <u>speed up</u> manufacture.

3) What is a <u>working triangle</u> in a kitchen?

4) Suggest how a good workplace layout can help with product <u>quality</u>.

5) Pete is designing the layout of his fish bicycle factory. Give two reasons why efficient <u>layout</u> of <u>materials</u> could help his manufacturing system to run smoothly.

CAD/CAM

CAD and CAM are a really important part of product design and manufacture.
They're used in lots of industries, from food production to graphic design.

CAD is Designing Using a Computer...

1) CAD stands for Computer Aided Design.

2) It involves designing products on a computer, rather than using a pencil and paper.

3) CAD packages include 2D drawing software (e.g. Adobe® Illustrator®, CorelDRAW®, TechSoft 2D Design® and ArtCAM®) and 3D modelling software (e.g. SolidWorks®).

4) CAD helps designers model and change their designs quickly. It's easy to experiment with alternative colours and forms and you can often spot problems before making anything.

5) In 3D programs, you can view the product from all angles.

...and CAM is Making Using a Computer

1) CAM stands for Computer Aided Manufacture.

2) It's the process of manufacturing products with the help of computers.

3) CAD software works out the coordinates of each point on the drawing. These are called x,y,z coordinates — x is the left/right position, y is forwards/backwards and z is up/down. The point where x, y and z meet is (0,0,0) — the datum.

4) CAM machines are computer numerically controlled (CNC) — they can follow the x,y,z coordinates and move the tools to cut out or build up your design.

5) For example, some milling machines are CAM machines. They remove material from a larger piece of material to shape and create a product.

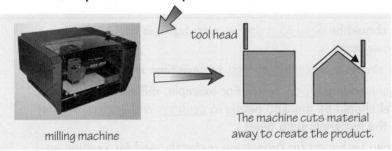

tool head

milling machine

The machine cuts material away to create the product.

6) Other examples of CAM machines are CNC routers, laser cutters and laser printers.

> CAM is useful for manufacturing at different scales...
>
> • individual items — laser-cutters are used to produce individual items like students' project pieces and 3D printers can be used to make one-off prototypes (see next page).
>
> • batches — you can draw your design once in CAD and then copy and paste the image so that the CAM machine will cut out more than one shape from your material at a time.
>
> • large quantities of the product — a CAM lathe works quickly and accurately to make large numbers of identical products, e.g. stair spindles for a furniture company.

Learn this CAD/CAM stuff — or you'll look like a right tool...

CAD and CAM are all the rage in product design circles these days. Everybody's at it — not surprising considering how useful they are. Sadly, that means examiners love testing you on it. Those cads...

CAD/CAM

CAM Machines Can be Used on Different Materials

1) There are CAM machines out there for all kinds of jobs — fear not...

2) Some CAM machines are 2-axis — they only use x and y coordinates so can only cut out 2D shapes.

3) Others are 3-axis machines — these use x, y, and z coordinates so they can cut out 3D shapes.

CNC routers are able to cut out either 2D or 3D shapes from a block of material using different sized cutting tools — they're either 2-axis or 3-axis machines. They can also be used to engrave things. CNC routers can be used on plastics, wood and metals.

Laser-cutters are used to cut and engrave things — they can be used on plastic, wood, cardboard, fabrics and some metals. Laser-cutters on high power settings cut right through the material. Lower power settings are used for engraving. Laser-cutters can only be used on sheet materials — they're 2 axis machines so they can't cut out 3D objects.

A net is just a 2D plan of a 3D object.

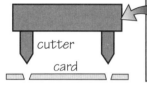

Die cutters are used to press out a net (e.g. for some packaging) from a sheet of material. They have a blade specially shaped to the outline of the net. You have to make a blade especially to match your net, so die cutting is expensive — but it's great for making large quantities of nets with complicated designs.

Vinyl cutters are used to cut out 2D shapes from thin sheet materials such as vinyl and card — they're 2 axis machines. They're often used to make signs and stencils.

3D printers can be used for rapid prototyping — they convert your design from an image on screen into a 3D model. Stereolithography and selective laser sintering can also be used for rapid prototyping but they're much slower and more expensive.

Practice Questions

1) a) What does CAD stand for?
   b) Give an example of a piece of 3D CAD software.
   c) Suggest why it might be a good idea to use CAD to design a product.

2) a) What is CAM?
   b) What is meant by CAM being 'computer numerically controlled'?

3) Give an example of how CAM can be used to make products:
   a) on an individual scale,
   b) in large quantities.

4) Why are 3D printers useful in the design process?

5) Billy decides to make a paperweight from a block of plastic, and package it in a cardboard box.
   a) Explain, with reasons, which CAM machine would be suitable for making the paperweight.
   b) Billy designs a net for the packaging.
      Suggest a CAM machine that could be used to cut it out from a sheet of card.

84

Consistency of Production

Manufacturers want their products to be consistent.
Jigs, templates and moulds help with this and also speed up the process.

Templates are Used to Make Repetitive Shapes

1) Templates are very easy to make and simple to use.

2) You can use them to reproduce any number of identical shapes from one original pattern (template). The template is used to draw or cut round. This saves a lot of time when you're marking out.

3) Templates need to be strong and hard-wearing — so that they can be used repetitively without getting damaged or worn.

4) Afterwards, the components can be checked against the templates for accuracy.

template

Jigs Help Manufacture Repetitive Components

1) A jig guides the tools that are working on a component, or makes sure that the workpiece is positioned in the right place.

2) Jigs come in many different shapes and sizes and can be specifically made for a particular job.

3) They're designed to speed up production and simplify the making process.

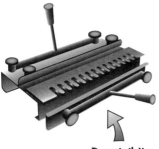
Dovetail jig

4) A drilling jig gets rid of the need for complex marking out. It guides the drill, which helps to cut down on errors, and makes sure every component is identical.

5) Jigs can help with complex cutting jobs too. E.g. a dovetail jig enables complex joints to be machined with a router, very quickly and easily, and with minimal measuring and marking out.

Moulds are Used to Reproduce 3D Shapes

1) Moulds are most commonly used in plastics manufacturing, in processes such as vacuum forming, compression moulding and blow moulding. See p. 74-75 for more on moulding.

2) Once an accurate mould has been made, detailed plastic shapes can be formed with it over and over again.

3) Industrial moulds can be expensive to produce (especially if they're made out of metal), so a manufacturer needs to be certain of the design. It's only cost-effective to make a mould if large numbers of a product are needed.

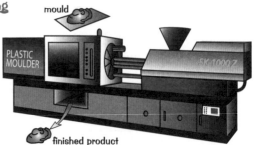
mould
PLASTIC MOULDER
SK-1000 Z
finished product

No — there's nothing on this page about Scottish dancing...

This stuff really is worth knowing about. You may well be asked to "Explain how to make a batch of..." That's your cue to show off your template and jig knowledge — so it'd be a shame if you couldn't.

Section 6 — Processes and Manufacture

Consistency of Production

CAD and CAM can also be used to make products consistent and accurate.

CAD/CAM can Improve Accuracy

1) Computer Aided Design (CAD) can let you see if components will fit together by modelling the design in 3D on screen. For example, if you're making a table you can see if the legs you designed will fit into the frame.

2) Computer Aided Manufacture (CAM) can also be used to model your designs. For example, you could use rapid prototyping (p. 83) to make a scale model to check that things are right before finalising the design.

3) CAD can help you to draw shapes accurately and you can quickly align things and alter sizes.

4) CAM is very accurate compared to doing the task by hand. For example, machines like laser-cutters can let you do very detailed work that would be very difficult by hand.

5) Using CAM machines to cut things out also means that each component is identical.

6) CAM reduces the amount of finishing — a laser-cutter gives an almost perfect edge when it cuts acrylic.

Repetiton is Easier Using CAD/CAM

1) Repeating patterns can be produced quickly for textiles or graphics, simply by copying and pasting the design in CAD — you don't need to draw them again and again.

2) You can also rotate and mirror things easily — a right-hand component can be designed by copying and flipping a left-hand one.

3) You only need to draw a component or product in CAD once, but it can be reproduced several times from the drawing. You just need to programme the CAM machine to cut out several copies of the design — usually just by a click of a button.

CAD/CAM Can be More Efficient Than People

1) CAD programmes can do things very quickly, e.g. shading drawings and calculating sizes.

2) Rather than having to redraw a design, changes can be made quickly and easily.

3) CAM machines are usually much quicker than doing the job by hand.

4) Machines don't take holidays, need sleep or get ill (although they can break down).

Practice Questions

1) Why must templates be hard-wearing?

2) How does a jig help when manufacturing identical components?

3) When might making a mould not be cost effective?

4) A furniture company is manufacturing a batch of wardrobes. Explain how CAM can be used to improve the quality of the batch.

5) Jenny is making a handbag with a repeating pattern of butterflies on it. Explain how CAD can speed up this process.

Exam Technique

1) The exam lasts 2 hours. There's one paper split into two sections.

2) Section A is the design question. Section B is a load of questions on anything and everything you've learned — materials, tools, environmental stuff, etc.

Section A is the Design Question

A bit before the exam, your teacher will give you a preparation sheet. This tells you what the theme of the design question will be. Use this to do some research and practise a few designs.

Section A is about designing.

You should spend about 30 minutes on this question.

1 Design a product for children and give some details about how it might be manufactured.

1 (a) Identify **three** design criteria which will make your product successful with the target market.
Give **two** reasons for each criteria.

The examiners suggest how long you should spend on each question — pay attention to this so you don't spend too long on one thing.

Design Criteria	Reason
Should be cheap to buy	1 To encourage parents to buy the product 2 To sell more items
Should be tough and hard-wearing	1 Needs to be able to stand up to child's play 2 Parents want a product that will last
Should be bright and colourful	1 To appeal to children 2 So that it stands out on the shop shelves

(9 marks)

Make sure you give the right number of answers — always read the question carefully.

The design criteria make up the design specification (see p. 7). You can give any criteria that match the design theme — just make sure they're sensible and you can back them up with good reasons.

There are 9 marks for this question — that's one for each criteria and one for each reason.

1 (b) In the space on the next page, develop a design for your product in enough detail for somebody else to be able to make it.

Marks will be awarded for:
i)   clarity of communication   (6 marks)
ii) creativity   (5 marks)
iii) feasibility of the design   (4 marks)

Pay attention to what the marks will be awarded for. The examiner is giving you some big hints here — make sure your design covers all these points fully.

Exam Technique

DESIGN IDEAS

Nylon bag

Plastic clasps

Zip fastening

Canvas bag

FINAL DESIGN

Clasps made from PET using injection moulding. Attached to adjustable nylon straps which are sewn onto the bag.

Bag to be made from nylon panels sewn together. Nylon is strong, tough, resistant to wear and easy to clean.

Simple clasps are easy for children to use.

Anna

Bold, bright colours appeal to children.

White panel for children to write their name. Bag will be sold with a non-toxic fabric marker pen.

Pocket sewn onto front

> You get marks for your work being <u>neat</u>, <u>nicely laid out</u> and <u>easy to understand</u>. You should also <u>add notes</u> to your design.

> <u>Sketch</u> a few ideas before deciding on one to <u>develop</u> — you get marks for showing you've developed your design.

> You need to show your design has been <u>well thought out</u>. For example, give details of <u>materials</u> and <u>manufacturing processes</u> — it must be possible to make it.

> You get marks for how <u>creative</u> and <u>interesting</u> your design is.

> Keep your <u>design criteria</u> and your <u>target market</u> in mind — this product is for children so it has to appeal to them.

> You'll get two blank pages to do your design — think about adding <u>dimensions</u>, showing your design from <u>different angles</u> or doing more <u>detailed drawings</u> of components, e.g. clasps.

1 (c) Evaluate the effectiveness of your design proposal against the criteria you gave in part (a).

I specified that the product should be cheap to buy.

The materials and manufacturing processes are

relatively inexpensive, so the product can be

produced and sold cheaply. Nylon is also a tough

material and should stand up to use by a child.

Finally, the fun, bright colours used for the bag should

make it appealing to children .

(6 marks)

> The question says '<u>evaluate</u>'. You need to give a <u>full explanation</u> for every point you make.

> In at least one of the questions (you'll be told which), **your <u>written communication</u>** skills will be tested. For these questions it's really important that you write in <u>full sentences</u> and check your <u>spelling</u> and <u>grammar</u>.

> You gave <u>three</u> criteria in part (a) — make sure you talk about <u>all</u> of them here.

Exam Technique

Here are some of the kinds of questions you'll face in <u>Section B</u>.

Section B <u>Covers</u> Everything

This question is about materials.

You are advised to spend about 15 minutes on this question.

2 (a) Choose a product from the table below. State the main material it's made from and list **two** properties of the material that make it suitable for the product.

Product	Material	Property of Material
	HDPE	1. Easy to mould
		2. Stiff and strong
		1.
		2.

(3 marks)

> In the exam, you'll probably be given a <u>wider range of products</u> made from a variety of <u>different</u> materials. Remember to pick the ones that you're <u>familiar</u> with.

> Be as <u>specific</u> as you can. Don't just say 'plastic' here — name the most likely <u>type</u>.

> To get both marks, make sure you list two <u>different</u> properties. You also need to make sure your answers are <u>relevant</u> to the particular product in the question.

> The question said to pick <u>one</u> <u>product</u> from the table, so you can just leave these boxes blank.

2 (b) Select **one** of the materials from the box below. Circle your choice.

polystyrene	(iron)	silk	oak

> Again, you can choose the material that you're most <u>familiar</u> with.

2 (b) (i) What is the source of the raw material?

Iron ore in the ground

(1 mark)

> Even if you think an answer is too <u>obvious</u> to be what the examiner wants, write it down anyway — some questions will be <u>easier</u> than others. There's no point looking for a more complicated answer.

2 (b) (ii) Briefly describe how the raw material is processed for manufacture into products.

The ore is crushed and heated in a blast furnace until it

melts. It is refined to remove any impurities and the

molten metal is poured into a mould and cooled (cast).

(3 marks)

> 'Briefly describe' means you don't need to go into too much detail, but make sure you've covered each stage. Look to see how many <u>lines</u> there are for your answer and try to <u>fill the space</u>.

Exam Technique

This question is about packaging and the environment.

You are advised to spend about 20 minutes on this question.

3   A company is trying to decide whether to package their new range of cupcakes in cardboard or plastic cartons.

3 (a) Name a suitable process for moulding a plastic carton.

Vacuum forming ....

(1 mark)

> You've got to think about <u>what's</u> being made — there are lots of different processes for moulding plastic, but the <u>best one</u> for making <u>plastic food cartons</u> is vacuum forming.

3 (b) Explain why cardboard might be considered a more environmentally friendly choice than plastic.

Cardboard is a sustainable material, as the trees cut

down to make it can be replaced. Cardboard is also

biodegradable. Plastic takes a long time to break down

and is made from crude oil, which is a finite resource.

(3 marks)

> This question is worth 3 marks so make sure you come up with at least <u>three</u> good <u>points</u>.

3 (c) The company decide to make their packaging from cardboard. They add the symbol below to the packaging. What does the symbol mean?

It means that the packaging is

made from recyclable cardboard.

(2 marks)

> There are 2 marks up for grabs here, so <u>don't</u> just put a one word answer. This recycling symbol is used <u>specifically</u> on cardboard.

This question is about the use of computers in product design and manufacture.

You are advised to spend about 15 minutes on this question.

4 (a) Give two advantages of using ICT in the design and manufacture of products.

Advantage 1 _Computer Aided Design (CAD) allows designers_

to quickly edit and manipulate designs, and make any changes

the client wants.

(2 marks)

> There are loads of things you could talk about here. The important thing is to make sure you <u>don't</u> just state <u>what</u> the advantage is — <u>explain why</u> it's an advantage too. That's what the <u>second mark</u> is for.

Advantage 2 _Computer Aided Manufacture (CAM) allows_

products to be machined at high speed. This means that lots

of products can be made in a short time period.

(2 marks)

> When you think you've <u>finished</u> the exam, go back and <u>read over</u> your answers to check for <u>mistakes</u>. You might even think of something else you could <u>add</u>.

90

Glossary

alloy	A mixture of <u>two or more</u> metals, or a metal mixed with other elements.
anthropometrics	<u>Body</u> measurement data.
batch production	The production method used to make a <u>specific number</u> of <u>identical</u> products.
binding	Binding is used to <u>hold sheets of paper together</u> in the form of a book.
biodegradable	Something that will <u>decay over time</u>. For example, paper and card are biodegradable but glass is not.
BSI	British Standards Institution. It <u>sets standards</u> for the <u>quality</u> and <u>safety</u> of products and methods. A product that meets these standards can display the <u>Kitemark</u>.
CAD/CAM	<u>Designing</u> and <u>manufacturing</u> using a <u>computer</u>.
carbon footprint	The amount of harmful <u>greenhouse gases</u> produced by manufacturing and using products.
components	The <u>different parts</u> that are assembled to make a product.
continuous production	Making large amounts of a product <u>non-stop</u>.
copyright	<u>Legal protection</u> which <u>prevents copying</u> of written, drawn or recorded work.
corrugated	With a <u>ridged</u> or <u>grooved surface</u>.
design brief	The <u>instructions</u> that the client gives to the designer about what they want the product to be like.
design specification	A list of <u>criteria</u> that a product should meet.
disassembly	Taking a product apart to see how it was <u>made</u>.
ergonomic	<u>Easy</u> and <u>comfortable</u> for people to <u>use</u>.
ferrous	Ferrous metals are ones that contain <u>iron</u>.
fibre	A thin, <u>hair-like strand</u>. Fibres can be spun into yarns and used to make fabrics. (In Food Technology, <u>dietary fibre</u> means a type of carbohydrate found in bran, wholewheat bread, etc.)
finishes	Finishes <u>protect a product</u> from dirt and damage and <u>improve its looks</u>.
finite	A finite resource is one that will <u>run out eventually</u>.
freehand	Drawing without using any <u>equipment</u> — only a pen or pencil.

Glossary

<u>Glossary</u>

Gantt chart	A time plan that shows how <u>long</u> different tasks will take and the <u>order</u> they need to be done in.
gsm	<u>Grams per square metre</u>, the way of showing the 'weight' of paper or board.
hardwood	Hardwood comes from trees with <u>broad leaves</u> (mainly deciduous trees, e.g. oak). It's usually denser and harder than softwood.
hazard	A potential <u>danger</u> to humans or the environment.
hue	Another word for <u>colour</u>.
ISO	International Standards Organisation. They issue <u>certificates</u> to organisations that meet international standards of <u>quality</u>.
laminated	<u>Covered</u> with a layer of <u>another material</u>.
market pull	When a product is made due to <u>consumer demand</u>.
market research	Asking the target market what they <u>like</u> or <u>dislike</u> about products, to help you with your design.
marketing	How companies try to <u>sell their products</u>, e.g. advertising, giving out free samples.
mass production	Used to produce a <u>large number of identical products</u> on a production line.
model	A <u>practice version</u> of a product that you make during the development stage. It's probably made from easy-to-work materials and might be scaled down in size.
non-ferrous	Non-ferrous metals are ones that <u>don't contain iron</u>.
one-off production	Making a <u>single</u>, often <u>unique</u> product.
orthographic projection	A <u>2D scale drawing</u> of a 3D object showing the front, plan and end views.
patent	<u>Legal protection</u> that prevents people copying the design of a new <u>invention</u>.
perspective drawing	Drawing <u>3D</u> objects so that things which are <u>further away</u> look <u>smaller</u>.
product analysis	<u>Examining</u> and <u>disassembling</u> a current product to get ideas for a new product or design.
prototype	A full-size, working, one-off model of a design. A prototype is built to allow <u>evaluation</u> of the product before starting manufacturing in quantity.
quality assurance	The <u>system</u> that is set up to make sure that <u>high quality</u> products are produced.

Glossary

quality control	The <u>checks</u> that are carried out on materials and products throughout production to make sure that standards are being met.
registered design	<u>Legal protection</u> that prevents someone copying a design's <u>shape</u> and <u>appearance</u>.
renewable	A renewable resource is one that can be <u>replaced</u> by natural processes as fast as it is <u>consumed</u> by humans, e.g. softwood trees in a plantation.
risk assessment	<u>Identifying</u> the <u>potential hazards</u> at each stage of production and the <u>precautions</u> which need to be taken to minimise risks.
sketch	A <u>simple, freehand drawing</u>.
smart materials	A material that <u>changes its properties</u> in response to a change in the environment.
softwood	Softwood comes from trees with <u>needle-like leaves</u> (mainly evergreen trees). It's usually <u>less dense</u> and easier to saw than hardwood.
sustainable	A sustainable process or material is one that can be used <u>without causing permanent damage</u> to the environment or <u>using up finite resources</u>. E.g. sustainable wood comes from forests where fast-growing trees are chopped down and replaced.
synthetic	A synthetic material is something that's <u>man-made</u>.
system	A collection of parts and processes that <u>work together</u> to do a particular job.
target market	The group of people you want to <u>sell</u> your product to.
technology push	When advances in technology drive the design of <u>new</u> products and the <u>redesign</u> of old products.
thermochromic	Thermochromic materials <u>change colour with heat</u>.
thermoplastics	Plastics that can be <u>melted and remoulded</u> over and over again.
thermosetting	Thermosetting plastics are ones that undergo a <u>chemical change</u> when heated which makes them hard and rigid. They can't be remoulded.
tolerance	The <u>margin of error</u> allowed for a measurement of part of a product. Tolerances are usually given as an upper and lower limit, e.g. 23 mm (± 2).
tone	How <u>light</u> or <u>dark</u> a colour is.
trademark	<u>Legal protection</u> that prevents people copying the <u>symbols</u>, <u>logos</u> or <u>slogans</u> that represent a company.
working drawing	A <u>detailed scale drawing</u> that shows all the dimensions of each part of a product, and the materials from which components are to be made, etc.

Answers

Page 3 — Evolution of Product Design

1) When a product is made due to consumer demand.

2) New technology might allow Arthur's MP3 player to be cheaper to produce, hold more songs and have better sound quality than older MP3 players.

3) a) E.g. wind-up radio
   b) E.g. fuel-efficient cars

4) a) Upright and angular.
   b) Bold colours, zigzag and stepped shapes, bold sweeping curves and sunburst motifs.
   c) Simple shapes, vertical and horizontal lines and primary colours.

5) Products should be designed with their job in mind, rather than their appearance.

Page 5 — Human Factors in Design

1) By having visual signs e.g. flashing lights.

2) To make them easy to find and press (so that the product is suitable for people with poor vision or limited movement in their hands).

3) E.g. Jewish people only eat Kosher food.

4) a) It could have a large, easy-to-grip handle.
   b) Infirm people might have difficulty holding and using a normal tin opener so a larger handle with grips would make it easier for them to use.

5) a) Ergonomics is about how easy and comfortable a product is to use.
   b) Anthropometrics need to be considered, e.g. the average size of people's hands. Its size and proportions need to fit the user and their needs, e.g. keys not too small and the keyboard should sit low on the desk. (Or similar answer.)
   c) They could experience long-term health effects e.g. hand strain, backache.

6) a) Body measurement data.
   b) E.g. chest size, collar size, height.
   c) The football shirt is probably designed to fit all but the smallest 5% and largest 5% of the target market — so it only fits 90% of the target market, not everybody.

Page 7 — Research and Specifications

1) a) E.g. what kind of product is needed, how the product will be used, who the product is for.
   b) the client

2) E.g. blue is the most popular colour. Most people think that the text is too small.

3) a) To find out about what people like/dislike about existing products. To see if people will want your product.
   b) How a product is made e.g. materials, what its good and bad points are, its size and weight and how it looks, feels, smells and tastes.

4) a) A list of conditions that the product must meet.
   b) E.g. must hold two eggs and four slices of toast, should have a shiny surface finish, must be easy to clean, no more than 10 cm tall, must cost less than £2 to manufacture.

Page 9 — Design Methods and Influences

1) a) This is the breaking down of the design process into different stages and doing each in turn.
   b) This is the use of trial and error to develop a good design.
   c) This involves experienced designers guessing what might work well in a design.

2) a) E.g. a flower, a leaf, a bird's nest.
   b) Red, orange and yellow are colours associated with fire and the sun, so using these could create a feeling of warmth in a room.

Page 11 — Practical Design and Modelling

1) It would help him to think about details of the design, e.g. the sizes and positions of its components and how they will fit together.

2) a) Modelling is when test versions of a design are made.
   b) E.g. cardboard, balsa wood

3) CAD can be used to make virtual models / to model designs in 3D. CAD/CAM can be used for rapid prototyping.

4) a) A full-size working product made before industrial production.
   b) To check the car works properly and is safe. Consumers might test the prototype — if it gets good feedback, the car might go into commercial production.

5) E.g. The radio should be made from cheap and readily available materials e.g. plastic, to reduce costs. It should use standard components where possible, to make production quick.

Page 13 — Presenting and Protecting Design Ideas

1) a) It is a distinctive logo, word or slogan that identifies a particular company or product.
   b) Unregistered trademarks are shown by ™, and registered trademarks by ®.
   c) E.g. Big Mac™ and Microsoft®.

2) a) To protect a new invention — people have to get permission and pay the inventor to use that idea.
   b) Patents are only given to ideas that involve an 'inventive step' — making a cardboard box is an old idea.

3) a) He could patent it.
   b) They would have to apply for permission to use the idea.

4) The firm he works for would own his idea.

5) It would protect the vacuum cleaner's shape and appearance from being copied by another company.

6) E.g. CAD could be used to make a realistic 3D drawing of how the trainers will look. It could also be used to produce accurate working drawings.

Page 15 — Working Schedules and Quality Control

1) a) It shows they have good quality assurance systems.
   b) Products are checked to see if they meet the manufacturer's specification.

2) E.g. 250 mm (±5)

3) a) Some of the processes can happen at the same time, e.g. making the table legs while the varnish is drying.
   b) 75 minutes
   c) Making the table legs — it takes 25 minutes.

Answers

Page 17 — Drawing Techniques

1) a) When you don't use any drawing equipment apart from a pencil/pen.
    b) Sketching initial design ideas.
    c) To explain details further, e.g. ideas for colours/materials.

2)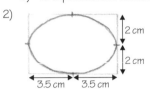

3) 30°

4) a) Crating is where you start by drawing a box and gradually add bits on and take bits off till you get the right shape.
    b) e.g.

    c) a wire frame

5) a) isometric drawing
    b)

Page 19 — Drawing Techniques

1) A point in the distance on the horizon line where 'parallel' lines appear to meet in a perspective drawing.

2) a) e.g.   b) e.g.

3) Front view, plan view and end view.

4) a) e.g. an exploded view
    b) They clearly show how the different parts should be assembled.

5) a) a sectional drawing
    b) E.g.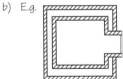

Page 21 — Drawing Enhancements

1)

2)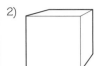

3) a) primary and secondary colours
    b) Add more white to make the tone lighter and add more black to make the tone darker.
    c) orange

Page 23 — Presentation Techniques

1) E.g. use coloured pencils — use more than one colour to get the right shade and use a darker colour to show the grain.

2) a) Any two of, e.g. marker pens / coloured pencils / poster paints
    b) Use water colour paints and add a bit of yellow.

3) highlights

4) a) e.g. SolidWorks® / Pro/DESKTOP®
    b) Any two of, e.g. by altering colours / by adding light and shadow effects / by creating a different background.

5) a) e.g. Paint Shop Pro / Adobe® Photoshop®
    b) E.g. the photo could be distorted / made to look like it's a pencil drawing.
    c) E.g. the colours could be changed.

Page 25 — Packaging and the Environment

1) Paper, textiles, plastic.

2) a) E.g. bubble wrap — the air inside the bubbles will help prevent the ornaments from getting broken if they're knocked.
    b) As a security / anti-theft device.

3) a) crude oil
    b) Corn starch — it's made from a renewable resource and it's biodegradable.

4) Any two of, e.g. plastic packaging uses up crude oil (which is a finite resource) / packaging ends up as waste, which is unsightly and may take a long time to break down / increased burning of fossil fuels to provide energy for packaging production causes air pollution and contributes to global warming.

5) Any three of, e.g. encourage customers to re-use bags / charge customers for bags so that they'll take fewer of them / use sustainable materials to make the bags / use recycled materials to make the bags / collect used carrier bags for recycling.

Page 27 — Labelling

1) a) the BSI Kitemark
    b) The product meets EU safety standards.
    c) Consumers tend to be more willing to buy approved products, or will pay more for them, so having these symbols can make products more profitable.

2) a) The products will be protected by copyright.
    b) GiantzComics™ is trademarked, which means other companies are not allowed to copy the name.

3) a) E.g. instructions for use, cleaning instructions, safety information.

Answers

b) E.g.

> Use with 230V mains supply.
> This product becomes very hot in use.
> Do not touch the heating plates.
> Not for use by children under 16 years.
> Do not leave unattended when switched on.
> Do not immerse in water. Wipe clean with
> a damp cloth when unplugged and cool.

Page 29 — Brands and Marketing

1) a) E.g. young adult males / rich professionals.
   b) E.g. car enthusiast magazines, men's magazines, billboards, television.
2) a) So that consumers can easily recognise their products.
   b) Any two of, e.g. food cartons / paper cups / paper napkins / staff uniforms / delivery van.
   c) The logo could be designed to appeal to young people, e.g. modern / fun design, bright colours etc.
3) a) E.g. a magazine for young people.
   b) Internet advertising can reach a wide audience and is quite cheap.
4) Use point of sale promotions such as signs in the shop aisle. Offer free samples of the beans for shoppers to try.

Page 31 — Properties of Materials

1) a) The material won't stretch / is likely to crack or break.
   b) The material can be moulded.
   c) The material can be drawn into wires.
2) a) e.g. a file / drill bit
   b) e.g. cutlery
   c) e.g. armour / bulletproof vest
3) E.g. bridge supports — need to resist squashing forces.
   E.g. surfboards — need to resist bending forces.
   E.g. drill bits — need to resist twisting forces.
4) Large items might be too expensive for anyone to buy if you make them from costly materials. / Many materials are only available in standard sizes.
5) Mass production is likely to use cheaper materials. If you're making a one-off product, you're more likely to use a more expensive material.
6 a) e.g. durable, strong, tough, smooth surface
   b) The material she chooses must be suitable for the manufacturing method she's planning to use.
   c) It would be expensive to use non-standard forms.

Page 33 — Paper and Card

1) a) textured
   b) e.g. sketching
2) They're both translucent / they both let light through.
3) gsm (grams per square metre)
4) E.g. secondary packaging to protect products during transport.
5) A3
6) a) aluminium
   b) It keeps flavours in and air out.

Page 35 — Timber

1) a) e.g. scots pine / parana pine
   b) e.g. scots pine — yellow with brown streaks / parana pine — yellow with red streaks
2) a) e.g. mahogany / beech
   b) e.g. red-brown (mahogany) / pinkish brown (beech)
3) They are slower growing.
4) To make it stronger and less likely to rot or twist.
5) Smooth the edges.
6) a) e.g. mahogany
   b) So that the grain will show.

Page 37 — Manufactured Boards

1) a)
   b) plywood
   c) It's more expensive.
2) They're mixed with glue and compressed.
3) a) e.g. building / construction
   b) e.g. cupboard backs / drawer bottoms
4) a) 2
   b) The paint might soak into the MDF.
5) By laminating with a hardwood veneer / By laminating with a 'hardwood effect' plastic laminate.

Page 39 — Metals

1) a) A metal that contains iron.
   b) Any two from, e.g. aluminium, zinc, copper, brass, silver, pewter.
2) a) It's made from a mixture of iron and carbon.
   b) e.g. brass, pewter
   c) It doesn't rust / corrode.
3) a) electrolysis / plating
   b) A corrosion-resistant metal, e.g. zinc, nickel.

Page 41 — Plastics

1) a) When they're heated they undergo a chemical change and become hard and rigid. Once you've heated and moulded them once they can't be melted and reshaped again.
   b) e.g. acrylic / polystyrene
2) E.g. melamine-formaldehyde — it will not melt when the pan gets hot.
3) a) It's durable / resistant to corrosion.
   b) Using wet and dry paper.
4) Crude oil is extracted from the ground. It's heated in a refinery which separates it into different chemicals by fractional distillation. Some of these chemicals (monomers) are then joined together by polymerisation to make plastics (polymers).

Page 43 — Ceramics

1) a) Any two from e.g. earthenware / stoneware / china clay / St Thomas' clay.
   b) It's dug from the ground

Answers

2) By altering the composition of the clay, e.g. by adding bentonite, flint or grog.

3) earthenware

4) Watered down clay. It's used to help stick bits of clay together.

5) E.g. to seal the surface / to give the bowl an attractive finish.

6) E.g. light bulbs — ceramics are heat-resistant / electricity pylons — ceramics are good insulators.

Page 45 — Textiles

1) Yarns are the threads that are spun from fibres. They're woven or knitted into fabrics.

2) Natural fibres are obtained from renewable sources (plants and animals). Synthetic fibres are made from finite resources, e.g. crude oil and coal.

3) Any two of, e.g. polyester / polyamide / acrylic / elastane (LYCRA®) / TACTEL®

4) a) Advantage — e.g. they don't fray when cut.
   b) Disadvantage — e.g. they're not stretchy / they're not very strong.

5) Bran. Or prunes. Depending on your taste.

Page 47 — Textiles

1) a) Any two of, e.g. it's strong / hard-wearing / comfortable / it feels cool in hot weather.
   b) Any two of, e.g. it creases / it's highly flammable / it has bad drape / it's expensive.

2) e.g. elastane

3) a) It can give you better properties.
   b) blending and mixing
   c) Blending is when two or more different fibres are combined to produce a yarn. Mixing is when a fabric is made up of two or more different types of yarn.

4) Any three of, e.g. flame retardant / water resistant / stain resistant / crease resistant / shrink resistant .

5) e.g. polyester and a flame retardant finish.

Page 49 — Food

1) e.g. potatoes and flour

2) To build and repair tissues, muscles and organs.

3) a) ascorbic acid
   b) e.g. citrus fruits / green vegetables / peppers / potatoes

4) a) Any two of, e.g. it's a preservative / it sweetens food / it caramelises when heated.
   b) Any two of, e.g. it adds flavour to foods like shortbread / it adds colour to pastry / it can be rubbed into flour to make pastry and biscuits crumbly.
   c) egg

Page 51 — Food

1) a) cereal grains, e.g. wheat or maize
   b) sugar beets

2) To lighten the flour.

3) To kill bacteria.

4) A 'set' material, in between a solid and a liquid.

5) a) An emulsion is formed when oily and watery liquids are mixed together and the droplets of one are spread through the other.
   b) Using an emulsifier, e.g. egg yolk.

Page 53 — Electrical Components

1) input, process, output

2) a) copper wire
   b) It's a good conductor of electricity.

3) light-dependent resistor

4) a) Thermistors (temperature sensors) change the resistance in a circuit depending on the temperature.
   b) buzzer

Page 55 — Mechanical Components

1) rotary and linear

2)

3) a) e.g. a single pulley / a block and tackle
   b) e.g. single pulley — changes the direction of the force required, so she can lift the load by pulling downwards. / Block and tackle — she only needs to use half the force she'd need otherwise.

4) a) Move the pivot closer to the load.
   b) first class

Page 57 — Fixings and Bindings

1) Any three of, e.g. double-sided sticky pads / ratchet rivets / post and screw fixings / snap rivets.

2) a) e.g. treasury tags / prong paper fasteners
   b) e.g. a drawing pin / velcro pads / a hook

3) a) e.g. saddle stitching / comb binding / spiral binding
   b) The pages are less likely to come loose.

Page 59 — Standard Components

1) a) Common fixings and parts that manufacturers buy instead of manufacturing them themselves.
   b) It saves time and money during manufacture.
   c) e.g. zips / buttons / thread

2) a) wood screws
   b) E.g. round / countersunk / slotted / cross.

3) a) Fittings which enable furniture to be assembled and taken apart easily.
   b) flat-pack furniture

4) joining sheet metal

Answers

Page 61 — New Materials

1) Cornstarch is made from plants, so it's a renewable material/is sustainable. It's also biodegradable.

2) The clay would be worked into the right shape. Then it would be heated to create a solid object. It could then be polished.

3) a) Smart materials react to their environment by changing their properties.
   b) thermochromic ink — it will change colour as the temperature increases.

4) A material made from very, very small particles.

5) E.g. he might have added an antibacterial coating.

6) a) E.g. using quantum tunnelling composite switches.
   b) E.g. heart rate/blood pressure sensors in clothes.

Page 63 — Safety

1) a) Protective gloves, apron, sometimes a face shield.
   b) Make sure there's enough ventilation, use a dust extractor and wear goggles.

2) Wear (rubber) gloves to protect his hands. Wear goggles in case any of the dye splashes onto his face. Ensure adequate ventilation so that the fumes don't build up.

3) Any four from, e.g. Don't leave the machine unattended while switched on. / Know how to switch off and isolate the machine in an emergency. / Don't change parts (e.g. drill bits) on a machine until you've isolated it from the mains. / Tie hair back. / Tuck ties and apron strings in.

4) During the design process and before manufacturing begins.

5) a) Brian, because he should have designed the teddy bear so that this could not happen / his design should have included a secure method of attaching the eyes
   b) E.g. Brian should have made a prototype of the design and tested it thoroughly.

Page 65 — Quality

1) Read some reports about cars in 'Which?' magazine/on the website of Which?.

2) a) the Sale of Goods Act
   b) the Fire Safety Regulations

3) A test of a component or product to make sure that it meets the manufacturing specification.

4) An international standard of quality management.

5) a) 15.4 cm by 10.4 cm
   b) 14.6 cm by 9.6 cm

Page 67 — Ethics and Environmental Issues

1) A resource that will eventually run out.

2) a) Designing products so that they become useless or go out of fashion quickly.
   b) Because more materials and energy have to be used to make replacement products.

3) E.g. the truck could be made from high-quality/durable materials and components, have parts (wheels, say) that can be replaced.

4) a) The amount of greenhouse gases released into the atmosphere by making or using a product.
   b) The distance a product travels from where it's made to where it's sold.
   c) Either 'John' or 'his neighbour' is acceptable with a reasonable explanation. E.g. 'John's fridge because if he keeps it for a long time it will use less energy over its whole life, causing less greenhouse gas emissions.' OR 'His neighbour's fridge, because it has many fewer product miles even if a bit more energy is needed to run it. '

5) E.g. recycle — he could use a plastic that is recyclable,
   refuse — he could keep packaging to a minimum,
   rethink — he could design a 'two in one' knife and spoon,
   etc.

Page 69 — Ethics and Environmental Issues

1) E.g. Pine/softwood — it's renewable because trees can grow as fast as we use them up. / Cotton/linen/wool/silk — it's renewable because cotton plants/flax plants/sheep/silkworms can grow as fast as we use the materials up.

2) A biodegradable material is something that breaks down naturally/rots away naturally.

3) a) No, because it's made of many different parts and three different materials.
   b) The varnish may give off toxic fumes (which may contribute to global warming).

4) Because materials have to be collected, transported and processed.

5) The farmers and workers who grew the rice were paid a fair price/ a price that covers the cost of sustainable production.

Page 71 — Tools

1) hacksaw

2) Cutting curves in wood and plastic.

3) bradawl

4) Any two from, e.g. countersink bit — for making holes for screw heads to sit in / flat bit — to drill large flat-bottomed holes / twist bit — for drilling small holes.

5) E.g. hand tool — bench plane, power tool — planer.

Page 73 — Forming and Bending

1) sheet metal folder

2) a) heat it or anneal it.
   b)

3) (Hot) metals are placed on it to be hammered into shape.

4) a) The strips of wood are glued together and held in a jig, which keeps them bent in the desired shape while the glue dries.
   b) E.g. rocking chair runners, chair/table legs.

5) a) line bending
   b) The element in the line bender heats the plastic along the line where you want to bend it. Once the plastic is soft, it can be bent.

98

Answers

Page 75 — Casting and Moulding

1) a) thermosetting plastics
   b) A 'slug' of thermosetting plastic powder is put into a 'female' mould. A former is pressed onto it and pushes the plastic into the mould. Very high temperatures and pressures liquefy the powder, and the plastic is set into a permanent shape.

2) A sheet of thermoplastic is heated until it goes soft. A mould is put onto the vacuum bed. The bed is then lifted close to the heated plastic. The air is sucked out from under the plastic. This forces the plastic onto the mould.

3) a) blow moulding
   b)

4) a) a mould
   b) metal and thermoplastics

5) a) a plastic
   b) Molten plastic is forced into a closed mould under pressure.

6) E.g. plastic covered wire, plastic/aluminium edgings.

Page 77 — Scale of Production

1) a) batch production
   b) So they can switch between making batches of different things.

2) a) mass production
   b) Most of the staff don't need to be highly skilled.

3) e.g. aluminium foil / chemicals / oil

4) a) A just-in-time system is where the manufacturer gets the materials and components delivered as they're needed and uses them as soon as they're delivered.
   b) E.g. because it saves on space for storing materials / there's less money tied up in materials that aren't being used / unsold finished products don't pile up.

5) E.g. he'd use CAM machines and use cheaper materials to make the process as cheap and efficient as possible.

Page 79 — Manufacturing Systems and ICT

1) A collection of parts and processes that work together to do a particular function.

2) Inputs, processes and outputs.

3) Systems make manufacturing processes more efficient and ensure that the final product is top class by building in feedback loops so that quality checks can be done.

4) E.g.

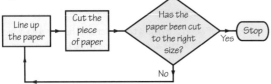

5) E.g. the designer can work in one location and easily transfer the work to the client in a different location using electronic data interchange. Meetings can be held using video conferencing. This would help the project move quickly and makes sure the final product turns out exactly how the client wants it to be.

Page 81 — Manufacturing Systems

1) Any four of, e.g. a trained and organised workforce / specialised buildings or workshops / good communication systems / organisation of tools, equipment and materials / efficient design and production processes / systems for disposing of waste / risk assessment and safety procedures.

2) The stages of the assembly line should be near to each other — areas should follow on from each other in the order of the manufacturing process. This minimises the time and energy wasted by people walking to different areas.

3) A plan of where to put the fridge, oven and sink in a kitchen so that workers don't have to walk far between them.

4) E.g. finishing areas (e.g. painting and varnishing) can be placed away from dusty work areas. Finished products can be stored near the dispatch area to reduce the distance they are carried — this helps to prevent damage.

5) E.g. workers will be able to find materials easily and it's easier to keep an eye on stock levels.

Page 83 — CAD/CAM

1) a) Computer Aided Design
   b) e.g. SolidWorks®
   c) E.g. you can change your design quickly / it's easy to experiment with alternative colours and forms / you can often spot any problems before you make your product.

2) a) Computer Aided Manufacture.
   b) The machines follow the x,y,z coordinates from the drawing, and move the tools to shape the material.

3) a) E.g. laser-cutters can be used to make individual items like students' project work / 3D printers can be used to make one-off prototypes.
   b) E.g. a CAM lathe can be used to make large quantities of identical products quickly and accurately.

4) You can use them for rapid prototyping — making a 3D model from a CAD design.

5) a) A CNC router because it can use x, y and z coordinates to cut out 3D shapes from a block of plastic.
   b) E.g. a die cutter

Page 85 — Consistency of Production

1) Because they're used over and over again.

2) It guides the tool and makes sure that every component is identical.

3) If only a small number of products are needed.

4) E.g. CAM machines are more accurate than doing the job by hand. Using CAM machines to cut things out also means that each component in the batch will be identical.

5) E.g. she can copy and paste the butterfly design using CAD, rather than having to draw the design over and over again.

Answers

Index

3D printers 83
3rd angle orthographic projections 15, 19

A

adverts 29
aeration 49
aesthetics 8
alloys 38
aluminium 38
annealing 39, 72
anthropometric data 5
assembly drawings 15, 18
assembly line 76, 81

B

batch production 76
bench grinder 71
bench plane 71
bevel gears 54
binding ingredients 49
bindings 57
blending fibres 46
blockboard 36
blocks in circuits 52
blowing agents 41
blow moulding 74, 84
board 32-33, 36-37
bolts 58
brace 70
brand image 28
brass 38
brazing 72
British Standards Institution (BSI) 26, 64
butter 49

C

cabinet rasps 71
CAD/CAM 10, 19, 76-77, 82-83, 85
capacitors 52
carbon footprint 66
card 32
cartridge paper 32
cast iron 38
'CE' mark 26
chain and sprocket mechanisms 55
chipboard 36
circuits 52
clay 42
CNC routers 82-83
coating food 49
cold chisels 71
colour in designs 9
colours in drawing 21
comb binding 57
commercial manufacturing 78
composites 33
compression moulding 84
concrete 43

consumer demand 2
continuous improvement 2
continuous production 76
copper 38
copyright 12, 26
corrosion 30, 41
corrugated board 32
crating 17
crude oil 41, 45
cultural values 4

D

data transfer 79
design
  brief 6
  criteria 7, 86, 87
  methods 8
  movements 3
  process 6
  specification 7, 86
die casting 74
die cutters 83
dovetail jig 84
drills 70
durability 30

E

eggs 49
electrical circuits 58
electrical systems 52
electrolysis 39
electronic data interchange (EDI) 79
empirical problem solving 8
emulsification 49
emulsions 51
end view 19
environmental issues 66-69
ergonomics 5
evaluation 10, 87
exploded views 18
extrusion 75

F

fair trade 69
fats 48-49
feedback loop 78
'female' mould 74
ferrous metals 38
Fibonacci series 9
fibre in food 48
fibres in fabrics 44-46
files 71
fillers 41
fixings 56
flour 50
flow charts 15
foam core board 33
food 48-51, 58
food components 50

forge 72
former 72, 74
fractional distillation 41, 45
freehand sketches 16
front view 19
fruit 50

G

Gantt charts 15
gear trains 54
gels 51
glass 43
glazing ceramics 42
glazing food 49
gouger 71
grid paper 32

H

hand tools 71
hardboard 36
hardening metals 39
hardwoods 34
hazard symbols 26
heat treatments 39

I

industrial moulds 84
injection moulding 75
input blocks 52
input devices 53
input motion 54
inputs in systems 78
insulators 52
integrated circuits 53
integrated electronics 61
intuitive designing 8
isometric drawings 16

J

jigs 72, 84
just-in-time (JIT) system 77, 79

K

kiln 42
knock-down fittings 59

L

labelling 26-27
lacquering 39
laminating 33, 73
laser cutters 82-83, 85
laser printers 82
lathe 71
layout paper 32
levers 54
linear motion 54
line bending 73
links 55

Index